Teacher Edition

STRATEGIES for Writers

Conventions & SKILLS

Practice Book

Level G

Authors

Leslie W. Crawford, Ed.D.
Georgia College & State University

Rebecca Bowers Sipe, Ed.D.
Eastern Michigan University

Editorial Development by Cottage Communications

Cover Design by Tommaso Design Group

Production by Marilyn Rodgers Bahney Paselsky

Zaner-Bloser, Inc., P.O. Box 16764, Columbus, Ohio 43216-6764 (1-800-421-3018)

ISBN 0-7367-1261-5

Printed in the United States of America

02   03   04   05   06   MZ   5   4   3   2   1

Unit 1
Sentence Structure

Unit 2
Parts of Speech

Unit 3
Usage

Unit 4
Grammar

Unit 5
Mechanics

Complete Subjects and Complete Predicates

Learn

The Constitution of the United States | set forth our country's basic laws.
              a.   **b.**

Which part, **a.** or **b.**, of this sentence tells whom or what the sentence is about? __a.__

Which part, **a.** or **b.**, tells what the subject does? __b.__

> Every sentence has a subject and a predicate. The **complete subject** is made up of a noun or pronoun and words that tell about it. The subject tells whom or what the sentence is about. The **complete predicate** is made up of a verb and words that tell what the subject is, has, or does.

Practice

Draw a line between the complete subject and the complete predicate in each sentence.

1. The U.S. Constitution | explains the organization and principles of our government.
2. The Constitution | was signed on September 17, 1787.
3. It | had been ratified by all the states in 1789.
4. Thirty-nine colonial patriots | put their signatures on the document.
5. These colonists | met at the Pennsylvania State House in Philadelphia, Pennsylvania.
6. That location | was renamed Independence Hall.
7. The signers of the Constitution | used a quill pen and a silver inkstand.
8. The same pen and inkstand | had been used for signing the Declaration of Independence in 1776.
9. Two of the signers | later became United States presidents.
10. They | were George Washington and James Madison.
11. One of the most famous signers of the Constitution | was Benjamin Franklin.
12. The Constitution | established a strong national government for our country.
13. The Constitution | is the basis for all of our nation's laws.
14. Its first ten amendments, the Bill of Rights, | guarantee certain rights for all citizens.

Write complete sentences by matching a complete subject in the first column with a complete predicate in the second column.

Complete Subjects

Thirty-nine delegates

The laws of the nation

A strong national government

The Pennsylvania State House

Both George Washington and James Madison

The Bill of Rights

Benjamin Franklin

The Preamble of the Constitution

Complete Predicates

was established by the Constitution.

are based on the Constitution.

is now Independence Hall.

became presidents of the United States.

guarantees certain freedoms for all citizens.

was one of the signers of the Constitution.

begins with the words "We the people."

signed the U.S. Constitution.

15. Thirty-nine delegates signed the U.S. Constitution.

16. The laws of the nation are based on the Constitution.

17. A strong national government was established by the Constitution.

18. The Pennsylvania State House is now Independence Hall.

19. Both George Washington and James Madison became presidents of the United States.

20. The Bill of Rights guarantees certain freedoms for all citizens.

21. Benjamin Franklin was one of the signers of the Constitution.

22. The Preamble of the Constitution begins with the words "We the people."

Simple Subjects and Simple Predicates

Learn

a. **One amendment to the Constitution** establishes freedom of the press.

b. Read all the amendments to the Constitution.

The complete subject of sentence **a.** is in boldfaced type.
Which word is the most important word in the complete subject? ____amendment____

Write the verb that tells what the subject of sentence **a.** does. ____establishes____

Can you find the subject at the beginning of sentence **b.**? ____no____
Circle the word that fits as the subject of sentence **b.**: Amendment   Freedoms   (You)   Read

> The **simple subject** is the most important word or words in the complete subject.
> It is a noun or pronoun and tells whom or what the sentence is about. The subject
> of a request or command (an imperative sentence) is usually not named. The
> person being spoken to, *you,* is the **understood subject**. The **simple predicate** is
> the most important word or words in the predicate. It is a verb. The simple
> predicate tells what the subject did or what was done to the subject. The simple
> predicate may also be a form of the verb *be.*

Practice

Underline the simple subject in each sentence. If the understood subject is *you,* write **you** on the line.
Circle the simple predicate.

1. The Constitution of our country was adopted in 1789. _____

2. The first ten amendments to the Constitution are called the Bill of Rights. _____

3. The freedoms of religion, speech, and the press are guaranteed by the First Amendment. _____

4. It also protects the rights of free assembly and petition. _____

5. The next two amendments involve issues regarding soldiers and militias. _____

6. Read the Sixth through the Ninth Amendments for information about other rights
of citizens. ____you____

7. The Ninth Amendment assures citizens of rights not specifically stated. _____

8. Study the amendment about double jeopardy. ____you____

9. Eighteen-year-olds gained the vote with the Twenty-sixth Amendment. _____

10. Other amendments have been proposed. _____

Write eight sentences about the amendments to the Constitution. The information in the Word Bank provides the ideas for the simple subject and simple predicates. Use the understood subject **you** in at least one of your sentences.   Answers will vary.

Word Bank

Twelfth Amendment, election of President and Vice President	guarantees
Thirteenth Amendment, abolition of slavery	shows
Fourteenth Amendment, civil rights	changes
Sixteenth Amendment, income taxes	gives
Nineteenth Amendment, right of women to vote	allows
Twenty-third Amendment, right to vote for citizens living in	provides
the District of Columbia	lists
Twenty-sixth Amendment, voting rights for 18-year-olds	establishes

11. _____

_____

12. _____

_____

13. _____

_____

14. _____

_____

15. _____

_____

16. _____

_____

17. _____

_____

18. _____

_____

Compound Subjects and Compound Predicates

Learn

   a. The Constitution gives rights to the people and provides responsibilities for the government.

   b. The Magna Carta and the Virginia Declaration of Rights were models for the Constitution.

Which sentence, **a.** or **b.**, has two or more simple subjects? __b.__

Which sentence, **a.** or **b.**, has two or more simple predicates? __a.__

> A **compound subject** contains two or more subjects joined by a conjunction (*and, or*). A **compound predicate** contains two or more verbs joined by a conjunction.

Practice

Each sentence below has either a compound subject or a compound predicate. If a sentence has a compound subject, circle the two or more nouns that are the simple subjects. If a sentence has a compound predicate, underline the two or more verbs that are the simple predicates.

  1. The framers of the Constitution debated and decided a number of important issues.

  2. The Fifteenth Amendment and the Nineteenth Amendment ensure the right to vote.

  3. The due process clause and the equal protection clause are found in the Fourteenth Amendment.

  4. Double jeopardy and cruel or unusual punishments are prohibited by the Constitution.

  5. The houses of Congress and the state legislators added amendments on voting rights.

  6. Amending the Constitution is complex and requires many steps.

  7. The writers wanted a difficult process and therefore created one.

  8. Lawmakers and all citizens must be very sure an amendment is good for the country.

  9. Freedom of speech and freedom of religion are not without limits.

10. A person may not slander another person or cause a riot.

11. The amendment giving women voting rights was proposed in 1919 and ratified in 1920.

12. The Twentieth Amendment and the Twenty-second Amendment specify the terms of the president.

13. The president is elected for four years and can be reelected once.

14. Two terms in office became law in 1951 and affected all future presidential elections.

15. The disability of the president and the succession to the office of president are covered in the Twenty-fifth Amendment.

Strategies for Writers—Conventions & Skills Practice **Unit I**   **11**

Combine each pair of sentences to form one sentence that has either a compound subject or a compound predicate. **Answers may vary. Possible responses appear below.**

16. The Preamble to the Constitution consists of one paragraph. It tells why the Constitution was written.

The Preamble to the Constitution consists of one paragraph and tells why the Constitution was written.

17. The Preamble is part of the Constitution. The Bill of Rights is also part of the Constitution.

The Preamble and the Bill of Rights are parts of the Constitution.

18. The legislative branch is part of the federal government. Another branch is the executive branch. There is also the judicial branch.

The legislative branch, the executive branch, and the judicial branch form the federal government.

[NOT "the legislative, the executive, and the judicial branches"]

19. The House of Representatives is part of the legislative branch. The Senate is also part of the legislative branch.

The House of Representatives and the Senate make up the legislative branch.

20. The president is part of the executive branch. The vice president is also part of the executive branch.

The president and the vice president are part of the executive branch.

21. The Supreme Court is part of the judicial branch. The other courts of the country are also part of the judicial branch.

The Supreme Court and the other courts of the country are parts of the judicial branch.

22. Each branch of the government checks the other branches. They balance each other's power.

Each branch of the government checks the other branches and balances the others' power.

23. People who are accused of crimes do not have to testify against themselves. Neither do they have to hire lawyers if they cannot afford to.

People who are accused of crimes do not have to testify against themselves or hire lawyers

if they cannot afford to.

Direct and Indirect Objects

Learn

The Emancipation Proclamation of 1863 gave the American **slaves hope** for freedom.

Which boldfaced word tells what the Emancipation Proclamation gave? _____ hope

Which boldfaced word tells to whom it was given? _____ slaves

> The **direct object** is the noun or pronoun that receives the action of the verb. Only action verbs can have a direct object. More than one object is a **compound direct object**. To find the direct object, say the verb and then ask "What?" or "Whom?" An **indirect object** is a person or thing to whom something is given, told, or taught. The indirect object is a noun or pronoun, and it comes before the direct object. To test whether a word is an indirect object, move it after the direct object and put the word *to* or *for* in front of it.

Practice

Underline the direct object in each sentence. Then circle any indirect object. Not all sentences have an indirect object.

1. During the American Civil War, President Abraham Lincoln issued a historic proclamation.

2. This Emancipation Proclamation gave the (slaves) freedom in the rebellious states of the Confederacy.

3. The Confederate states left the Union in 1861.

4. The Confederate states no longer gave the (Union) their allegiance.

5. Therefore, the Emancipation Proclamation did not give immediate freedom to slaves in the South.

6. The Thirteenth Amendment to the United States Constitution released all slaves from slavery.

7. This 1865 amendment advanced the rights of all people.

8. The Constitution did not give (African Americans) the right to vote until 1870.

9. The Fifteenth Amendment gave African American (men) the right to vote.

10. It did not provide African American (women) the same right, however.

11. The Nineteenth Amendment finally gave all (women) the vote in 1920.

12. Even with these constitutional guarantees, local laws and customs often denied (African Americans) many rights.

Strategies for Writers—Conventions & Skills Practice Unit 1

Rewrite the sentences in order to change the boldfaced words into indirect objects. Then underline the direct objects in your sentences. **Answers may vary. Possible responses appear below.**

13. Civil rights laws give basic rights **to all citizens**. _____

Civil rights laws gave all citizens basic <u>rights</u>.

14. These rights guarantee certain freedoms **for all of us**. _____

These rights guarantee all of us certain <u>freedoms</u>.

15. For many years, laws denied some rights **to many Americans**. _____

For many years, laws denied many Americans some <u>rights</u>.

16. In 1939, a group denied a chance to sing at Constitution Hall **to singer Marian Anderson**.

In 1939, a group denied Marian Anderson a <u>chance</u> to sing at Constitution Hall.

17. Instead, she gave a successful concert **for her audience** at the Lincoln Memorial.

Instead, she gave her audience a successful <u>concert</u> at the Lincoln Memorial.

18. In 1963, President Lyndon Johnson awarded the Medal of Freedom **to Marian Anderson**.

In 1963, President Lyndon Johnson awarded Marian Anderson the <u>Medal of Freedom</u>.

19. In 1944, the city of St. Louis, Missouri, first gave permission **to all its citizens** to eat together.

In 1944, the city of St. Louis, Missouri first gave <u>permission</u> to eat together to all its citizens.

20. Some people have given the title "Mother of the Modern Civil Rights Movement" **to Rosa Parks**.

Some people have given Rosa Parks the <u>title</u> "Mother of the Modern Civil Rights Movement."

21. In 1955, some bus riders refused a seat in the front of the bus **to her**. _____

In 1955, some bus riders refused her a <u>seat</u> in the front of the bus.

22. She was arrested for not giving her seat **to a white person**. _____

She was arrested for not giving a white person <u>her seat</u>.

23. All of these events teach important lessons **to all of us**. _____

All of these events teach all of us important <u>lessons</u>.

Prepositional Phrases

Learn

Women in the United States could vote after August 18, 1920.

Where were the women? _____ in the United States

When could the women vote? _____ after August 18, 1920

> A **prepositional phrase** can tell *how, what kind, when, how much,* or *where.*
> A prepositional phrase begins with a **preposition,** such as *in, over, of, to,* or *by.*
> It ends with a noun or pronoun that is the **object of the preposition**. The words
> between the preposition and its object are part of the prepositional phrase. A
> prepositional phrase can appear at the beginning, middle, or end of a sentence.

Practice

Underline each prepositional phrase. Circle the preposition and draw a box around the object of the preposition. There may be more than one prepositional phrase in each sentence.

1. A movement for women's voting rights had been active for a long time before 1920.

2. Women could vote in some western states of the United States.

3. Wyoming was the first state in the United States to give women the vote.

4. For that reason, Wyoming is called "The Equality State."

5. The National American Woman Suffrage Association was formed with a major goal for women.

6. Susan B. Anthony was the second president of the organization.

7. In 1875, she suggested the wording of an amendment to the Constitution.

8. She worked with the next leader of the organization, Carrie Chapman Catt.

9. Between the years of 1910 and 1912, six more western states gave women the vote.

10. In 1913, women in Illinois could vote for president but not for members of Congress.

11. Suffragist parades in big cities drew the attention of large numbers of people.

12. In 1916, Jeanette Rankin was elected to Congress.

13. Three years later, Congress approved the women's suffrage amendment in a close vote.

14. The wording of the amendment was the same as that written by Susan B. Anthony 44 years earlier.

Use each prepositional phrase in a sentence about voting rights. You may add additional prepositional phrases to the sentence. **Answers will vary.**

15. for many years _____

_____

16. through the years _____

_____

17. in the nineteenth century _____

_____

18. for voting rights _____

_____

19. with determination _____

_____

20. by Congress _____

_____

21. in the nation _____

_____

22. during their struggle _____

_____

23. in some western states _____

_____

24. at the parades _____

_____

25. by two votes _____

_____

26. after all these years _____

_____

Appositives

Learn

a. Theodore Roosevelt was the twenty-sixth president of the United States.

b. Theodore Roosevelt, the twenty-sixth president of the United States, took office at the age of 42.

Underline the phrase in sentence **b.** that tells who or what Theodore Roosevelt was.

What punctuation marks separate this phrase from the rest of the sentence? _____commas_____

> An **appositive** is a phrase that identifies a noun. An appositive follows the noun it identifies and is usually separated from the rest of the sentence by commas.

Practice

Circle the appositive in each sentence. Draw an arrow from the appositive to the noun it identifies. The noun might be a person's name.

1. Theodore Roosevelt became president when McKinley, the twenty-fifth president, was assassinated.

2. William McKinley and Roosevelt took office in 1901, the first year of the twentieth century.

3. People were excited to be entering the twentieth century, a time of historic change.

4. Queen Victoria, the longest reigning British monarch, was nearing the end of her reign.

5. Australia, the only country that is also a continent, had become the Commonwealth of Australia the previous year.

6. Australia, a former British colony, became a federation of six states.

7. The English monarch, Queen Victoria, had given Australians the right to self-government.

8. In 1900, Russia was still under the rule of Nicholas II, the last Russian czar.

9. In China, the empress dowager, Ci Xi, ruled the country even though her son was the emperor.

10. Sultan Abdul-Hamid II, the head of the Ottoman Empire, continued to rule over a large but diminishing empire.

11. It has been said that three fifths of the world's population, about 960 million people, fell under the rule of four heads of government.

12. However, the governments of Russia, China, the Ottoman Empire, and even England, the super-powers of the day, were about to lose their dominance.

13. Meanwhile, President Theodore Roosevelt, "Teddy," brought a new outlook to the United States.

Apply

Rewrite each pair of sentences as one sentence. Change the underlined sentence into an appositive.

14. Roosevelt worked to protect the nation's resources. <u>Those resources were the forests and the water supplies.</u>

     Roosevelt worked to protect the nation's resources, the forests and the water supplies.

15. A cartoonist showed Roosevelt holding a small animal. <u>The animal was a bear cub.</u>

     A cartoonist showed Roosevelt holding a small animal, a bear cub.

16. Now Teddy Roosevelt is remembered for a toy. <u>The toy is the teddy bear.</u>

     Now Teddy Roosevelt is remembered for a toy, the teddy bear.

17. Queen Victoria became queen when she was eighteen. <u>This was a young age for a monarch.</u>

     Queen Victoria became queen when she was eighteen, a young age for a monarch.

18. She reigned for 63 years. <u>This is one of the longest reigns in history.</u>

     She reigned for 63 years, one of the longest reigns in history.

19. An inventor sent the first telegraph message across the Atlantic Ocean in 1901. <u>He was Guglielmo Marconi.</u>

     An inventor, Guglielmo Marconi, sent the first telegraph message across the Atlantic Ocean in 1901.

20. The first flight by Orville Wright occurred early in the twentieth century. <u>The date was December 17, 1903.</u>

     The first flight by Orville Wright occurred early in the twentieth century, December 17, 1903.

21. American inventors were experimenting with a revolutionary machine. <u>It was the automobile.</u>

     American inventors were experimenting with a revolutionary machine, the automobile.

22. The first company to mass-produce cars produced 425 cars in 1901. <u>The company was the Olds Motor Works.</u>

     The first company to mass-produce cars, the Olds Motor Works, produced 425 cars in 1901.

Kinds of Sentences

Learn

Many young women went to Atlantic City in 1921 to be in a contest. What were they there for? Read on to find out. It was the first Miss America contest!

Write the end mark that follows the statement. __.__

Write the end mark that follows the question. __?__

Write the end mark that follows the command. __.__

Write the end mark that follows the sentence that shows excitement. __!__

> A **declarative sentence** makes a statement and ends with a period. An **interrogative sentence** asks a question and ends with a question mark. An **imperative sentence** gives a command and ends with a period or an exclamation point. An **exclamatory sentence** shows excitement and ends with an exclamation point. Begin every sentence with a capital letter.

Practice

Add the correct punctuation mark to each sentence. Then label the sentence **dec** (declarative), **int** (interrogative), **imp** (imperative), or **exc** (exclamatory).

1. The first Miss America was Margaret Gorman, a 16-year-old __.__   dec

2. What do you think the contestants wore __?__   int

3. Look at the pictures of them __.__   imp

4. Wow, those knee-high stockings with the bathing suits are amazing __!__   exc

5. The 1920s in the United States were called the Roaring Twenties __.__   dec

6. Were the 1920s filled with interesting events __?__   int

7. Was Gertrude Ederle the first woman to swim the English Channel __?__   int

8. She swam 35 miles in an incredible $14\frac{1}{2}$ hours __.__   dec

9. Consider another event from that era __.__   imp

10. On October 29, 1929, the value of the stock market suddenly fell __.__   dec

11. What a great shock it was __!__   exc

12. Do you think the 1920s were an interesting time __?__   int

Apply

Rewrite each sentence to make it the type of sentence indicated in parentheses.

13. You can read about the events of the 1920s. (imperative) _____

Read about the events of the 1920s.

14. Were the 1920s full of contradictions? (declarative) _____

The 1920s were full of contradictions.

15. In the 1920s there were more freedoms and more fears than in the previous ten years. (interrogative)

Were there more freedoms and more fears in the 1920s than in the previous ten years?

16. Didn't women gain the right to vote in 1920? (declarative) _____

Women gained the right to vote in 1920.

17. On October 29, 1929, prices on the N.Y. Stock Exchange dropped by $14 million. (exclamatory)

On that terrible day, October 29, 1929, prices on the N.Y. Stock Exchange dropped by a shocking $14 million!

18. There were other factors that created the Great Depression. (interrogative) _____

Were there other factors that created the Great Depression?

19. Wasn't the world just recovering from World War I? (declarative) _____

The world was just recovering from World War I.

20. Was Europe devastated? (exclamatory) _____

Europe was absolutely devastated!

21. Did U.S. president Warren Harding promise "a return to normalcy"? (declarative)

U.S. president Warren Harding promised "a return to normalcy."

22. Normalcy wasn't as easy as Harding had hoped. (exclamatory) _____

Normalcy wasn't as easy as Harding had hoped!

23. Do you remember that time cannot go backwards? (imperative) _____

Remember that time cannot go backwards.

24. The war had taken its toll, and the country was on a new course. (interrogative) _____

Had the war taken its toll, and was the country on a new course?

Simple Sentences and Compound Sentences

Learn

   a. The League of Nations sought international cooperation (and) world peace.
   b. The League of Nations was established in 1919, (but) it was dissolved in 1946.

Circle the boldfaced conjunction in each sentence.
Which sentence, **a.** or **b.**, could be written as two separate sentences? ___**b.**___

> A **simple sentence** is made up of a subject and a predicate and expresses only
> one complete thought. It is an *independent clause*. A **compound sentence** is
> made up of two closely related independent clauses. The two clauses can be
> joined by a comma and a coordinating conjunction (*and, or,* or *but*) or by a
> semicolon (*;*).

Practice

Write **S** after each simple sentence. Write **CD** after each compound sentence. Circle the comma and
conjunction or the semicolon that joins the independent clauses in each compound sentence.

  1. After World War I, the victorious countries held a meeting.   _____S_____

  2. France, Great Britain, Italy, Japan, and the United States drew up a plan for the
      League of Nations.   _____S_____

  3. President Woodrow Wilson favored the agreement, but the United States did
      not join the League.   _____CD_____

  4. Forty-three nations were original members; other nations joined later.   _____CD_____

  5. Members of the League promised peaceful relations with other members.   _____S_____

  6. Both Japan and Germany withdrew in 1933, and Italy withdrew in 1937.   _____CD_____

  7. These withdrawals weakened the League; the support of powerful countries was needed.   _____CD_____

  8. There was a crisis over Italy's domination of Ethiopia in 1936, and the League of
      Nations could not ease the crisis.   _____CD_____

  9. World War II broke out in 1939 with Germany's attack on Poland.   _____S_____

 10. The League of Nations had been unable to prevent another large-scale war.   _____S_____

 11. After W.W. II, nations sought a lasting peace, but many thought that impossible.   _____CD_____

 12. In June of 1945, fifty nations signed the charter of the new United Nations.   _____S_____

Apply

Answers may vary. Possible responses appear below.

Rewrite each pair of simple sentences as one compound sentence.

13. The Charter of the United Nations is its constitution. It explains the rules of the organization.

The Charter of the United Nations is its constitution; it explains the rules of the organization.

14. The Security Council's role is peacekeeping. Nations bring their disputes to this body.

The Security Council's role is peacekeeping; nations bring their disputes to this body.

15. There are five permanent members of the Security Council. Ten additional members are elected for two-year terms.

There are five permanent members of the Security Council, and ten additional members are elected for two-year terms.

16. The Secretariat provides service to all the other organs of the UN. The secretary-general and other administrators make up the Secretariat.

The Secretariat provides service to all the other organs of the UN; the secretary-general and other administrators make up the Secretariat.

17. Another UN organ is the Economic and Social Council. This organ works for improved social and economic conditions in the world.

Another UN organ is the Economic and Social Council; it works for improved social and economic conditions in the world.

18. The UN has its headquarters in New York. The International Court is located in The Hague in the Netherlands.

The UN has its headquarters in New York, and the International Court is located in The Hague in the Netherlands.

19. There are many committees and agencies of the UN. Most of them are part of the Economic and Social Council.

There are many committees and agencies of the UN, and most of them are part of the Economic and Social Council.

20. The UN is not always successful in preventing armed conflicts. It does hold out the possibility of world peace.

The UN is not always successful in preventing armed conflicts, but it does hold out the possibility of world peace.

Complex Sentences

Learn

Although we think of baseball as a modern sport, it has been around for many years.
      a.   **b.**

Look at the two parts of this sentence. Which part, **a.** or **b.**, makes sense by itself? ___**b.**___

> A **complex sentence** is made up of an **independent clause** and at least one
> **dependent clause**. A dependent clause has a subject and a predicate, but it must be
> joined with an independent clause to make sense. A dependent clause begins with a
> subordinating conjunction, such as *although, because, if, as, when,* or *while.*

Practice

Underline each independent clause. Circle each dependent clause. Draw a box around the
subordinating conjunction that begins each dependent clause.

1. Baseball was developed in the United States, although it is based on an English game
   called rounders.

2. The game we know was developed in the 1800s, although rounders had been played in England
   as early as the 1600s.

3. In the 1700s, the American colonists helped establish the game in the U.S. when they played
   rounders.

4. This is one theory of baseball's beginning, although another theory says that Abner Doubleday
   invented the game in 1839.

5. That theory is no longer popular because the game Doubleday "invented" was very similar to
   rounders.

6. Alexander Cartwright became an important figure in the history of the game when he set
   many of the rules in 1845.

7. If you have heard of the Knickerbocker Base Ball Club, you might know about
   Alexander Cartwright.

8. This club of Cartwright's is remembered because it was the first one with the purpose of just
   playing baseball.

9. As the game began to grow in popularity, many other baseball clubs were formed.

10. The Civil War in the 1860s created more interest in the game when Union soldiers played
    the game for recreation.

      Strategies for Writers—Conventions & Skills Practice   Unit I   **23**

Write your own sentences by adding an independent clause to each dependent clause below. You may use the dependent clause at the beginning or the end of the sentence. **Answers will vary.**

11. as the batter stepped up to the plate _____

_____

12. if you like baseball _____

_____

13. when the great Babe Ruth came up to bat _____

_____

14. because nearly everyone loves watching the game _____

_____

15. as the game became more popular _____

_____

16. if you go to a baseball game today _____

_____

17. when you go to a game _____

_____

18. as more teams were formed _____

_____

19. because so many people pay attention to baseball games _____

_____

20. if there's another baseball strike _____

_____

21. as more cities got their own teams _____

_____

22. although every player is important to the team _____

_____

23. when players stayed with one team _____

_____

Avoiding Fragments, Run-ons, and Comma Splices

Learn

a. The Seven Wonders of the Ancient World are outstanding sights, some of these magnificent structures still exist today.

b. Because they were built between 3000 B.C. and A.D. 476.

Which sentence, **a.** or **b.,** is a dependent clause that is missing an independent clause? ____**b.**____

Which sentence is written incorrectly because it has two independent clauses without a conjunction? ____**a.**____

> A **fragment** does not tell a complete thought. A **run-on sentence** is a compound sentence that is missing a comma and a conjunction. A **comma splice** is a run-on sentence that has a comma but is missing a conjunction.

Practice

Write **F** after each fragment. Write **RO** after each run-on sentence. Write **CS** after each comma splice. If the sentence is written correctly, write **OK**.

1. The pyramids of Egypt at Giza were built in ancient times, they are still standing today. _**CS**_

2. They were built as tombs for kings, but thousands of workers were needed for their construction. _**OK**_

3. These tombs are the oldest of the wonders they were built four to five thousand years ago. _**RO**_

4. The largest pyramid has more than two million stone blocks, each stone weighs more than two tons. _**CS**_

5. The Hanging Gardens of Babylon by King Nebuchadnezzar II. _**F**_

6. The gardens are on top of buildings, water had to be lifted to keep the gardens alive. _**CS**_

7. The king married a princess who had lived in mountain country, he probably had the gardens built to remind her of the mountains. _**CS**_

8. The Temple of Artemis at Ephesus was built around 550 B.C. it burned in 356 B.C. _**RO**_

9. The Greek city of Ephesus which is in modern-day Turkey. _**F**_

10. The tall pillars were made of marble; the roof had tile-covered wood. _**OK**_

11. A famous statue of Zeus at Olympia in Greece. _**F**_

12. Although it was probably built about 435 B.C. _**F**_

Apply

Answers will vary. Possible answers appear below.

Rewrite the ten items from the Practice exercises that you marked **F, RO,** or **CS** to make them correct. There may be more than one correct way to write the sentences.

13. The pyramids of Egypt at Giza were built in ancient times, and they are still standing today.

14. These tombs are the oldest of the wonders. They were built four to five thousand years ago.

15. The largest pyramid has more than two million two-ton stone blocks, and each stone weighs more than two tons.

16. The Hanging Gardens of Babylon were built by King Nebuchadnezzar II.

17. The gardens are on top of buildings, so water had to be lifted to keep them alive.

18. The king married a princess who had lived in mountain country; he probably had the gardens built to remind her of the mountains.

19. The Temple of Artemis at Ephesus was built around 550 B.C. and burned in 356 B.C.

20. The Greek city of Ephesus is in modern-day Turkey.

21. A famous statue of Zeus was found at Olympia in Greece.

22. It was probably built about 435 B.C.

Common and Proper Nouns

Learn

Almost every **visitor** to the **United States** wants to see the **Grand Canyon** at some **time**.

Underline the boldfaced words that name a particular person, place, thing, or idea.

> A **common noun** names any person, place, thing, or idea. A **proper noun** names a particular person, place, thing, or idea. Proper nouns must be capitalized. A proper noun made of several words (*James Madison* or *West Bridgewater Middle School*) is considered one proper noun.

Practice

Write **C** if the boldfaced words are common nouns. Write **P** if they are proper nouns.

1. **Grand Canyon National Park** consists of more than a million acres.   P

2. This canyon is not as deep as Snake River Canyon in Idaho or **Copper Canyon** in Mexico.   P

3. However, **geologists** think it is one of the most fascinating places in North America.   C

4. The various layers of exposed rocks along the walls of the **canyon** provide scientists with a view into the past.   C

5. The canyon lies within the **Colorado Plateau,** an area that has many high plateaus.   P

6. Parts of several states, including New Mexico and **Arizona,** are in this area.   P

7. Scientists agree that this is one of the best places in the United States to study the geological **history** of our country.   C

8. Some of the **Grand Canyon's** oldest rocks are found in the inner gorge.   P

9. They may be as old as two billion **years,** which is older than the Rocky Mountains.   C

10. Many early explorers, including **John Newberry,** were impressed by the Grand Canyon.   P

11. Later, people discovered that the rocks were older than the **Colorado River** itself.   P

12. The Colorado River now ends in the **Gulf of California,** but that gulf is not very old, according to geologists.   P

13. They believe that two different **rivers** may have joined somewhere near the Kaibab Plateau.   C

Apply

Rewrite each sentence, replacing the boldfaced words with proper nouns. Use words from the Word Bank or your own words. Be sure to capitalize the first word of each sentence.

Word Bank

Utah	Yellowstone National Park	Mammoth Cave	Arizona
Africa	Glen Canyon Dam	the Grand Canyon	Lake Powell
Earth	the Colorado River	the National Geographic Society	

14. The surface of **our planet** changes. _____
    The surface of Earth changes.

15. **A major river** affects the area around it. _____
    The Colorado River affects the area around it.

16. The water can move rocks and soil from **one state** to **another state**. _____
    The water can move rocks and soil from Utah to Arizona.

17. The moving and eroding rocks have carved out **a canyon**. _____
    The moving and eroding rocks have carved out the Grand Canyon.

18. **A dam** will affect water movement in the river. _____
    The Glen Canyon Dam will affect water movement in the river.

19. **A lake** was created by a dam; other lakes were formed from a glacier or a natural basin.
    Lake Powell was created by a dam; other lakes were formed from a glacier or a natural basin.

20. **One continent** has all three kinds of lakes. _____
    Africa has all three kinds of lakes.

21. **A park** has underground water that forms geysers and mudpots. _____
    Yellowstone National Park has underground water that forms geysers and mudpots.

22. Underground water has also formed **a cave**. _____
    Underground water has also formed Mammoth Cave.

23. **An organization** can give you more information about these places. _____
    The National Geographic Society can give you more information about these places.

Singular and Plural Nouns

Learn

To a **scientist**, the natural **world** consists of **animals**, **vegetables**, and **minerals**.

Underline the boldfaced nouns that name a single person, place, or thing.

> A **singular noun** names one person, place, thing, or idea. A **plural noun** names more than one. Most nouns add -s or -es to form the plural. The spelling of some nouns changes when -es is added to form the plural (*sky/skies; wolf/wolves*). A few nouns do not add -s or -es to form the plural; instead, they change spelling (*woman/women*). A few other nouns have the same form in the singular and the plural (*deer/deer*).

Practice

Underline each singular noun. Circle each plural noun.

1. The world of nature has many inhabitants.
2. Zoologists classify animals into different groups.
3. At one time, there were only two main groups, animals and plants.
4. To many people, an animal is a mammal.
5. Your neighbor may think of a fox or a horse.
6. To a scientist, however, a mosquito and a turkey are also animals.
7. Scientists see animals as amphibians, fish, mammals, birds, reptiles, or invertebrates.
8. Each group is divided into still smaller groups.
9. For example, a mammal that eats insects is not in the same category as a mammal that eats meat.
10. Most animals have no backbones or internal skeletons.
11. This information surprises most people.
12. Insects do not have skeletons inside their bodies.
13. Instead, an insect has an external skeleton made from a hard material.
14. A mollusk also has a hard external skeleton, or shell.
15. The skeletons of all animals shape and protect their bodies.

Apply

Rewrite each sentence. Change the noun in parentheses to its correct plural form.

16. Biology is one of my favorite (class). _____

Biology is one of my favorite classes.

17. To me, scientists are true (hero) in our (community). _____

To me, scientists are true heroes in our communities.

18. Consider what their (belief) have added to our knowledge. _____

Consider what their beliefs have added to our knowledge.

19. Charles Darwin has a group of (finch) named after him. _____

Charles Darwin has a group of finches named after him.

20. Jean Fabre studied the (life) of bees, wasps, and grasshoppers. _____

Jean Fabre studied the lives of bees, wasps, and grasshoppers.

21. Rachel Carson warned of poisons in rivers, lakes, and other (body) of water. _____

Rachel Carson warned of poisons in rivers, lakes, and other bodies of water.

22. Although rats, (mouse), and (mosquito) may be small, they can carry and spread (disease).

Although rats, mice, and mosquitoes may be small, they can carry and spread diseases.

23. Such (study) help (man), (woman), and (child). _____

Such studies help men, women, and children.

24. A scientist is not merely a person who is good at taking (quiz) at (academy).

A scientist is not merely a person who is good at taking quizzes at academies.

25. Scientists are people who use logical (process) to learn about the world. _____

Scientists are people who use logical processes to learn about the world.

26. Often scientists make (discovery) by accident. _____

Often scientists make discoveries by accident.

27. There are many (story) about scientists and the (way) their minds work. _____

There are many stories about scientists and the ways their minds work.

28. Ordinary (person) see a dozen (sheep) and say they have long wool. _____

Ordinary persons see a dozen sheep and say they have long wool.

Copyright © Zaner-Bloser, Inc.

Singular Possessive and Plural Possessive Nouns

Learn

A **camera's** lens has an opening that controls the amount of light that enters.

Circle the part of the boldfaced word that shows ownership.

> A **possessive noun** shows ownership. **Singular** nouns add an apostrophe and *-s* to form the possessive (*worker/worker's*). Most plural nouns add an apostrophe after the *s* to form the possessive (*workers/workers'*). Plurals that don't end in *s* (*men/mice*) add an apostrophe and *-s* (*men's/mice's*) to show possession.

Practice

Underline each possessive noun. Write **S** if it is singular and **P** if it is plural. There may be more than one possessive noun in a sentence.

1. Your eyes' ability to see depends on many things.   P

2. The lens's ability to focus is important.   S

3. The eyeball's shape determines whether you are nearsighted or farsighted.   S

4. Your retinas' rods and cones send impulses to the brain.   P

5. Some people's retinas work but the pathway to the brain is damaged.   P

6. A person's ability to move both eyes at the same time also affects vision.   S

7. An eye doctor's examination will look at all these factors.   S

8. Before an eye examination, your pupils' normal movements are stopped.   P

9. Usually, a pupil's size is determined by the amount of light that enters.   S

10. Sometimes, people's emotions can influence the size of their pupils.   P

11. Doctors also check an eye's reflexive ability, which is how well it can adjust its focus.   S

12. Some families' members have some form of color blindness.   P

13. A man's inability to see certain colors is more common than a woman's.   S, S

14. A color-blind man's daughter will probably see all the colors, but her son's color sensitivity may be limited.   S, S

15. People's ability to see color is sometimes limited, but it is rarely a total loss.   P

Apply

Rewrite each sentence. Replace the underlined words by using possessives.

16. The brain of a person must interpret what the retina sees. _____

    A person's brain must interpret what the retina sees.

17. For example, the movements of people on film are not real. _____

    For example, people's movements on film are not real.

18. The surface of a film is made up of many still photographs with spaces between them.

    The film's surface is made up of many still photographs with spaces between them.

19. In other words, the edges of the photographs do not run together on the film.

    In other words, the photographs' edges do not run together on the film.

20. The image on each photograph is slightly different from the one before. _____

    Each photograph's image is slightly different from the one before.

21. The speed of a film is usually about 24 frames a second. _____

    A film's speed is usually about 24 frames a second.

22. However, the response of your eye is not fast enough to see each image separately.

    However, your eye's response is not fast enough to see each image separately.

23. The empty spaces on films do not register with the brain, so the pictures seem to run together.

    Films' empty spaces do not register with the brain, so the pictures seem to run together.

24. If you looked at a piece of film, you would see the blastoff of a rocket is made up of many separate images.

    If you looked at a piece of film, you would see a rocket's blastoff is made up of many separate images.

25. In a theater, the speed of the images creates the feeling of movement. _____

    In a theater, the images' speed creates the feeling of movement.

Personal Pronouns

<u>I</u> am reading a book about Marie Curie.

Underline the word in the sentence that shows who is speaking.

> A **pronoun** can take the place of a noun. **Personal pronouns** can be used to stand for the person speaking, the person spoken to, or the person spoken about. **First person** pronouns refer to the speaker (*I, me*) or include the speaker (*we, us*). **Second person** pronouns refer to the person being spoken to (*you*). **Third person** pronouns refer to the person, place, or thing being spoken about (*he, him, she, her, it, they, them*).

Practice

Underline each personal pronoun. Write **1** if it is a first person pronoun, **2** if it is second person, or **3** if it is third person.

1. <u>You</u> will find this book interesting.   2

2. <u>It</u> describes the life and works of Marie Curie.   3

3. <u>She</u> was born in Poland in 1867.   3

4. <u>I</u> cannot tell you how hard Marie and Pierre Curie worked.   1

5. The two of <u>them</u> were working with a substance called pitchblende.   3

6. <u>They</u> were inspired by the earlier work of Henri Becquerel, a French physicist.   3

7. In 1896, <u>he</u> had noticed unusual rays coming from uranium.   3

8. This discovery inspired the Curies, and <u>it</u> made Marie want to find similar rays.   3

9. The pitchblende caused sores on Marie's hands, and today <u>we</u> know why.   1

10. Pitchblende is mainly uranium oxide, and <u>it</u> burned <u>her</u>.   3, 3

11. Marie thought that if the pitchblende could burn her hands, <u>it</u> might also burn cancerous cells.   3

12. <u>She</u> and Pierre were refining the ore into separate elements.   3

13. <u>One</u> of them turned out to be radium.   3

14. The discovery was worth millions of dollars, but the Curies refused to patent <u>it</u>.   3

Strategies for Writers—Conventions & Skills Practice   **Unit 2**   **33**

Apply

Complete each sentence by writing the type of personal pronoun indicated.

15. This decision is one reason why _____ they _____ interest me so much. (third-person plural)

16. Did _____ you _____ know that Marie Curie died from leukemia? (second person)

17. Long exposure to radiation probably gave it to _____ her _____. (third-person singular)

18. Since the Curies worked together, the Nobel Prize went to both of _____ them _____. (third-person plural)

19. _____ We _____ know many details, because Marie kept a journal. (first-person plural)

20. The Curies' experiments took place inside an old shed, and _____ it _____ was described as "miserable" by Marie. (third-person singular)

21. Still, it seems to _____ me _____ that the dirt floor and leaky roof did not slow down the two scientists. (first-person singular)

22. Here _____ they _____ first saw the lovely blue glow of radium. (third-person plural)

23. Marie was delighted, since Pierre had said, "_____ I _____ should like radium to have a beautiful color." (first-person singular)

24. The discovery had taken _____ them _____ many years of work. (third-person plural)

25. Someone told _____ me _____ that Marie won another Nobel Prize in 1911. (first-person singular).

26. Marie Curie introduced the word *radioactivity*; now _____ it _____ is part of our everyday vocabulary. (third-person singular)

27. I wonder if _____ you _____ have heard of curium, an artificial element that was named for the Curies. (second-person singular)

28. Lisa Meitner is another woman physicist who helped discover a natural element and had an artificial element named for _____ her _____. (third-person singular)

29. However, Otto Hahn received the Nobel Prize for the element _____ she _____ helped him discover. (third-person singular)

30. I think I know why _____ we _____ hear a lot about the Curies and very little about Lisa Meitner. What do you think is the reason? (first-person plural)

Adjectives and Adverbs

Learn

Very heavy steel can float if it is the right shape.

Which boldfaced word describes a noun? _____heavy_____

Which boldfaced word tells about an adjective? _____very_____

> **Adjectives** describe nouns and pronouns. Some adjectives, like *colorful* and *memorable*, **describe** or tell **what kind**. Others, like *many* and *six,* tell **how many**. The **articles** *a, an,* and *the* are also adjectives. **Adverbs** modify verbs, adjectives, or other adverbs. They tell **how, when, where,** or **to what extent (how much)**. Many adverbs end in *ly*. Other common adverbs are *fast, very, often, again, sometimes, soon, only, too, later, first, then, there, far,* and *now.*

Practice

Underline each boldfaced word that is an adjective. Circle each boldfaced adjective that is an article. Draw two lines under each boldfaced word that is an adverb.

1. **Most** scientists **have** heard **of** Archimedes.

2. He was a **legendary** scientist who **lived** in ancient **Greece**.

3. **One** day, Archimedes **took** (a) bath.

4. He **climbed** into a deep tub and **soon** noticed (an) interesting detail.

5. Water **suddenly** spilled over the **edge** of the tub.

6. He recognized **then** a relationship **between** (the) spilling water **and** his mass.

7. According to one **famous** story, Archimedes **immediately** ran out and **shouted** "Eureka!"

8. On that day, he had discovered (an) **important** principle, called the buoyancy **principle**.

9. Have you **sometimes wondered** why a heavy **boat** floats?

10. A **huge** lump of **steel** would **quickly** sink.

11. However, a steel boat **usually** has a **long,** broad **shape**.

12. (The) weight of the steel is spread **over** (a) large **area** of water.

13. The boat **displaces,** or takes (the) place of, the water that was **there**.

Follow the directions to write each sentence. Include adjectives and/or adverbs in each sentence. You may use adjectives or adverbs from the Word Bank or choose your own. **Answers will vary.**

Word Bank

a	deep	safe	expensive	flat
an	heavy	dangerous	yellow	hollow
slowly	quickly	many	now	two
extremely	often	once	completely	finally

14. Describe a raft. _____

_____

15. Tell how it moves in the water. _____

_____

16. Tell what you could do on a raft. _____

_____

17. Tell how a ship and a raft are different or alike. _____

_____

18. Describe a water skier. _____

_____

19. Tell what happens when a boat runs aground. _____

_____

20. Describe what happens if there is too much weight in a boat. _____

_____

21. Tell one thing a good swimmer must do. _____

_____

22. State one good water safety rule. _____

_____

23. State one thing a swimmer should avoid. _____

_____

Action Verbs and Linking Verbs

Learn

Mr. Hosmer drew a triangle on the board.
A triangle is a figure with three sides and three angles.

Which verb shows action? _____ drew _____

Which verb links the subject of the sentence to words in the predicate that rename and describe it?

_____ is _____

> An **action verb** shows action. It usually tells what the subject of a clause is doing, will do, or did. An action verb may include one or more helping verbs in addition to the main verb. A **linking verb** does not show action. It connects the subject of a sentence to a word(s) that describes or renames the subject. Linking verbs are usually forms of *be*. Some common linking verbs are *am, is, are, was, were, been,* and *will be.* The verbs *become, seem, appear,* and *look* can also be used as linking verbs. A linking verb may include one or more helping verbs in addition to the main verb.

Practice

Underline each verb or verb phrase. Be sure to include any helping verbs you find. Write **A** if a verb is an action verb. Write **L** if it is a linking verb.

1. Our class has studied polygons. — A

2. Polygons are flat, closed figures with three or more straight sides. — L

3. Most people recognize triangles instantly. — A

4. However, many students become confused about different kinds of triangles. — L

5. I can identify an equilateral triangle every time. — A

6. All the sides and all the angles will be equal. — L

7. A right triangle has an angle of 90 degrees. — A

8. Obtuse triangles appear lopsided to me. — L

9. I defined the word *perimeter* correctly. — A

10. The perimeter is the distance around the sides of a figure. — L

11. Some people call it an outer boundary. — A

Apply

Write an action verb or a linking verb from the Word Bank to complete each sentence.

Word Bank

look	drew	will multiply
displayed	is called	is
are	will draw	will calculate
has	seems	appears
can measure	discussed	

12. You _____ can measure _____ the perimeter with simple addition.

13. Anyone _____ can calculate _____ the area as well.

14. The important measurements _____ are _____ the length of the base and the height.

15. Then you _____ multiply _____ these two numbers and divide by two.

16. Quadrilaterals _____ are _____ four-sided polygons.

17. Lauren _____ displayed _____ a chart about polygons.

18. The class _____ discussed _____ the difference between rectangles and squares.

19. A square _____ is _____ a type of rectangle.

20. Barry _____ will draw _____ a rectangle with four equal sides and four equal angles.

21. What polygons did you get when you _____ drew _____ a line from corner to corner in the square?

22. Now someone _____ will calculate _____ the area of the square.

23. That person _____ will multiply _____ the length of one side by itself.

24. Many rectangles _____ look _____ longer or wider than squares.

25. This rectangle _____ appears _____ twice as long as it is high.

26. Most parallelograms, however, _____ seem _____ tilted to one side.

27. A hexagon _____ has _____ six sides.

28. Did you know that a twelve-sided polygon _____ is called _____ a dodecahedron?

Active Voice and Passive Voice

Learn

a. Most people in the world use the metric system.

b. However, in the United States, another system is used by most people.

Underline the simple subject in each sentence.

In which sentence, **a.** or **b.**, does the subject do something? ___a.___

In which sentence, **a.** or **b.**, is something done to the subject? ___b.___

> If the subject performs an action, the verb is said to be in the **active voice**. (*Most people use . . .*) If the subject is acted upon by something else, the verb is said to be in the **passive voice**. (*. . . another system is used . . .*) Many sentences in the passive voice have a prepositional phrase that begins with the word *by* and follows the verb.

Practice

Write **A** if the main verb in the sentence is in the active voice. Write **P** if the main verb in the sentence is in the passive voice.

1. In 1975, the Metric Conversion Act was passed by the U.S. Congress. ___P___

2. This act encourages everyone to use the metric system. ___A___

3. The metric system is used by most countries today. ___P___

4. Most people in the United States do not use the metric system. ___A___

5. Instead, the U.S. Customary System is followed by almost everyone. ___P___

6. Under the U.S. Customary System, objects are measured in inches and feet. ___P___

7. Yards, rods, furlongs, and miles are also used by U.S. citizens. ___P___

8. Everyone must remember odd measurements, such as 1,760 yards to a mile. ___A___

9. The metric system, however, is remembered more easily. ___P___

10. Only one unit of length, the meter, must really be learned. ___P___

11. The metric system uses the decimal system. ___A___

12. The names of all metric units include the word *meter*. ___A___

13. Prefixes, such as *deca-*, *kilo-*, and *mega-*, must be remembered. ___P___

Strategies for Writers—Conventions & Skills Practice Unit 2

Rewrite each sentence so the verb is in the active voice. Answers will vary. Possible responses appear below.

14. Measurements have been used by people for centuries. _____

People have used measurements for centuries.

15. A report on measurements was given by Rita. _____

Rita gave a report on measurements.

16. The first standards were established by Egyptians and Babylonians. _____

Egyptians and Babylonians established the first standards.

17. Parts of the body were used as units of measurement by Egyptians. _____

Egyptians used parts of the body as units of measurement.

18. Many legends about measurements are told by scholars. _____

Scholars tell many legends about measurements.

19. King Henry I has been referred to by many sources. _____

Many sources have referred to King Henry I.

20. Supposedly, the length of a yard was established by King Henry I. _____

King Henry I supposedly established the length of a yard.

21. This standard was adopted by the colonists who came to America. _____

The colonists who came to America adopted this standard.

22. The original system was later changed by Americans. _____

Americans later changed the original system.

23. Today the metric system is used by most scientists. _____

Today most scientists use the metric system.

24. The U. S. Customary System is embraced by most nonprofessionals. _____

Most nonprofessionals embrace the U.S. Customary System.

25. The metric system is taught by many mathematics teachers. _____

Many mathematics teachers teach the metric system.

26. Metric tools are used by auto mechanics. _____

Auto mechanics use metric tools.

The Simple and Perfect Tenses

Learn

Rainbows **fascinate** people. I **had** always **loved** pictures of rainbows but had never seen one until recently. Now I **have seen** several. At this rate, I **will have seen** a dozen by the end of the month.

Which boldfaced verb tells about an action:

- that was completed by a certain time in the past? _____ had loved _____

- that will be complete by a certain time in the future? _____ will have seen _____

- that started in the past and was recently completed or is still happening? _____ have seen _____

A **present-tense verb** indicates that something happens regularly or is true now. A **past-tense verb** tells about something that happened in the past. Regular verbs form the past tense by adding -ed (*watch/watched*). The spelling of most irregular verbs changes in the past tense (*fly/flew*). A **future-tense verb** tells what will happen in the future. Add the helping verb *will* to the present tense form of a verb to form the future tense (*pass/will pass*). The **present perfect tense** (*have gained*) shows action that started in the past and was recently completed or is still happening. The **past perfect tense** (*had watched*) shows action that was completed by a certain time in the past. The **future perfect tense** (*will have passed*) shows action that will be completed by a certain time in the future. To form perfect tenses, use a form of *have* with the past participle of a verb.

Practice

Underline the word or phrase in parentheses that identifies the tense of each boldfaced verb.

1. I **had enjoyed** my visit to Hawaii. (past/<u>past perfect</u>)

2. My photo album **stays** on a table in the living room. (future/<u>present</u>)

3. By next week, you **will have seen** my picture of the rainbow. (<u>future perfect</u>/future)

4. We **have learned** a lot about rainbows in science class. (past perfect/<u>present perfect</u>)

5. Daylight **appears** white or colorless to the naked eye. (<u>present</u>/past)

6. A prism **will split** up the light into seven colors. (<u>future</u>/future perfect)

7. People **called** this group of colors a spectrum. (past perfect/<u>past</u>)

8. The raindrops **have acted** just like a prism. (present/<u>present perfect</u>)

9. Rainbows **had formed** around waterfalls in Hawaii. (<u>past perfect</u>/present perfect)

10. If you see an arch of colors at night, you **will have seen** a moonbow. (future/<u>future perfect</u>)

Apply

Rewrite each sentence, replacing each underlined verb with the same verb in another tense. Replace present tense verbs with the present perfect tense. Replace past tense verbs with the past perfect tense. Replace future tense verbs with the future perfect tense.

11. Aristotle <u>wrote</u> about weather phenomena. _____

Aristotle had written about weather phenomena.

12. Moonbows <u>appear</u> less often than rainbows. _____

Moonbows have appeared less often than rainbows.

13. Viewers <u>will see</u> moonbows only on nights with a full moon. _____

Viewers will have seen moonbows only on nights with a full moon.

14. The campers <u>watched</u> the moon rise. _____

The campers had watched the moon rise.

15. The full moon <u>rises</u> in the eastern part of the sky. _____

The full moon has risen in the eastern part of the sky.

16. The moonbow <u>formed</u> just before dawn. _____

The moonbow had formed just before dawn.

17. At dawn the moonlight <u>will shine</u> on the back of a rain cloud. _____

At dawn the moonlight will have shone on the back of a rain cloud.

18. Fogbows <u>display</u> no color. _____

Fogbows have displayed no color.

19. A fogbow <u>arched</u> across a foggy road. _____

A fogbow had arched across a foggy road.

20. You <u>will notice</u> a ghostly white band of light. _____

You will have noticed a ghostly white band of light.

21. Sun dogs <u>gleamed</u> low in the sky. _____

Sun dogs had gleamed low in the sky.

22. We <u>asked</u> what a ring around the moon forecasts. _____

We had asked what a ring around the moon forecasts.

Coordinating and Subordinating Conjunctions

Learn

A human body has cells, tissues, organs, **and** systems. We are learning about cells first **since** they are the smallest units. Most students know what cells are, **but** they do not really understand them.

Which boldfaced word links nouns? _____and_____

Which links two independent clauses? _____but_____

Which begins a dependent clause? _____since_____

> **Coordinating conjunctions** (*and, but, or*) connect words or groups of words (including independent clauses) of equal importance. **Subordinating conjunctions,** such as *although, because, since, so, if*, and *before*, connect a dependent clause with an independent clause. Subordinating conjunctions are used at the beginning of dependent clauses.

Practice

Underline the coordinating and subordinating conjunctions in these sentences. If a sentence contains a coordinating conjunction, write **C**. If it contains a subordinating conjunction, write **S**.

1. Although most cells are microscopic, scientists know a lot about them.   S

2. A cell might be shaped like a column, a sphere, or a cube.   C

3. Some cells, such as nerve cells, live for years, but others live only a few days.   C

4. A cell usually contains a membrane, cytoplasm, and a nucleus.   C

5. The cell membrane is important because it protects a cell.   S

6. Before a substance can enter a cell, receptors in the membrane identify the substance.   S

7. The substance may pass through the membrane, or it may be blocked.   C

8. If a cell had no cytoplasm, it could not function.   S

9. Cytoplasm allows a cell to make, change, and store proteins.   C

10. The nucleus is critically important because it contains genetic information.   S

11. If the nucleus of a cell is removed, the cell cannot reproduce.   S

12. The nucleus contains chromosomes, and the chromosomes contain genes.   C

Rewrite each pair of sentences as one sentence. Use a conjunction from the Word Bank in each. If you use a coordinating conjunction to join sentences, remember to write a comma before the conjunction. **Answers may vary. Possible responses appear below.**

Word Bank

and   or   but   if   so   since   because   although

13. Human cells contain 46 chromosomes. These chromosomes are arranged in pairs. _____

Human cells contain 46 chromosomes, and these chromosomes are arranged in pairs.

14. A gene may be dominant. A gene may be recessive. _____

A gene may be dominant, or it may be recessive.

15. A recessive gene is weaker than a dominant gene. A dominant gene will override a recessive gene.

A recessive gene is weaker than a dominant gene, so a dominant gene will override a recessive gene.

16. You might have one brown-eyed parent. You might have one blue-eyed parent. _____

You might have one brown-eyed parent, and you might have one blue-eyed parent.

17. The gene for brown eyes is dominant. Most brown-eyed parents have brown-eyed children.

Since the gene for brown eyes is dominant, most brown-eyed parents have brown-eyed children.

18. Both brown-eyed parents may carry recessive genes for blue eyes. They can have a blue-eyed child.

Because brown-eyed parents may carry recessive genes for blue eyes, they can have a blue-eyed child.

19. Some people have recessive genes. They do not know they have them. _____

Some people have recessive genes, but they do not know they have them.

20. A trait can come from a parent. A trait can come from a genetic mutation. _____

Although a trait can come from a parent, it can come from a genetic mutation.

21. Some diseases are genetic. Scientists want to learn more about them. _____

Some diseases are genetic, and scientists want to learn more about them.

Correlative Conjunctions

Learn

When you present this many figures, use either a <u>table</u> or a <u>bar chart</u>.

Which word joins the two underlined nouns? ___*or*_____

Which other word helps this word show how the nouns are linked? ___*either*_____

> **Correlative conjunctions** always appear in pairs. They connect words or groups of words and provide more emphasis than coordinating conjunctions. Some common correlative conjunctions are *both/and, either/or, neither/nor, not only/but (also)*, and *whether/or*.

Practice

Underline the correlative conjunctions and coordinating conjunctions in these sentences. If a sentence contains correlative conjunctions, write **CC** on the line.

1. Scientists often present not only written descriptions of experiments but also supporting data.   CC

2. Whether the data is easily understood or confusing may depend on its presentation.   CC

3. Large lists of numbers may confuse readers, but a chart can help readers understand the information.   _____

4. Charts can organize numbers and help readers see relationships among them.   _____

5. For example, you can present information by means of a table, a pie chart, a line graph, or a bar graph.   _____

6. Neither a pie chart nor a bar graph is perfect for everything.   CC

7. However, a good chart is both visually appealing and rapidly understood.   CC

8. If you are making comparisons, use either a pie chart or a bar graph.   CC

9. Bar graphs are probably the easiest and most useful.   _____

10. A bar graph displays amounts and allows viewers to instantly compare them.   _____

11. For instance, a bar graph might show either a general rise or fall in cancer cases.   CC

12. A pie chart not only shows amounts but also indicates percentages.   CC

13. A viewer can see instantly whether a dollar amount is a large percentage of the total budget or just a fraction of it.   CC

Rewrite each sentence pair as one sentence using the correlative conjunctions in parentheses. There is more than one way to join some sentence pairs. **Possible responses appear below.**

14. When you make a pie chart, you might limit the number of categories. Another choice is to provide a written summary. (either/or)

    When you make a pie chart, you might either limit the number of categories or provide a written summary.

15. First, you must decide if you will create a bar graph. You must decide if you will create a pie chart. (whether/or)

    First, you must decide whether you will create a bar graph or a pie chart.

16. Bar graphs can be vertical. Bar graphs can be horizontal. (either/or) _____

    Bar graphs can be either vertical or horizontal.

17. A line graph can display two kinds of information. It can also show trends. (both/and)

    A line graph can both display two kinds of information and show trends.

18. This line graph is hard to read because it has no grid lines. It also has no horizontal scale. (neither/nor)

    This line graph is hard to read because it has neither grid lines nor a horizontal scale.

19. This double bar graph is very colorful. It displays a lot of information. (not only/but also)

    This double bar graph is not only very colorful but also displays a lot of information.

20. This graph showed the number of students who bought lunch. It showed what they bought. (both/and)

    This graph showed both the number of students who bought lunch and what they bought.

21. You can make charts on a computer. You can draw them manually. (not only/but also)

    You can not only make charts on a computer but also draw them manually.

Buy and *By*

Learn

There is a store **by** the bus stop where we can **buy** a street map.

Which boldfaced word means "purchase"? _____buy_____

Which boldfaced word means "near"? _____by_____

> The words **buy** and **by** sound alike but have different meanings and spellings. *Buy* is a verb that means "purchase." The past-tense form is *bought*. *By* is a preposition that has several meanings, including "near or close to," "not later than," "through the action of," "with the use or help of," and "past." *By* can also be an adverb that means "nearby" or "past."

Practice

Underline the word in parentheses that correctly completes each sentence.

1. Today, you can (buy/by) many different kinds of maps.

2. If you travel (buy/by) bus, you need a map that shows bus routes.

3. A topographical map can show a hill (buy/by) a stream.

4. Sailors can (buy/by) nautical maps that show harbors, water depths, and buoys.

5. I saw a buoy when we crossed the bay (buy/by) ferry.

6. Some smaller boats sailed (buy/by), but they did not need maps.

7. The map that most people (buy/by) is probably the road map.

8. Usually we travel (buy/by) the routes that an automobile club suggests.

9. Many road maps have mileage indicators (buy/by) major highways.

10. Some road maps even show where travelers can (buy/by) gasoline or food.

11. If you (buy/by) an atlas, it will probably have at least three kinds of maps.

12. Political maps divide the world (buy/by) countries.

13. Our class should be finished drawing maps (buy/by) next week.

14. The climate map that is over (buy/by) the window is mine.

15. I would like to (buy/by) a frame for it someday.

Rewrite each sentence, replacing the boldfaced words with **buy** or **by**.

16. You can **purchase** maps at many bookstores. _____

You can buy maps at many bookstores.

17. Do you see the globe **near** the window? _____

Do you see the globe by the window?

18. It is **next to** the bookcase that holds a big atlas. _____

It is by the bookcase that holds a big atlas.

19. People **pay money for** globes because they are more accurate than flat maps. _____

People buy globes because they are more accurate than flat maps.

20. **Through the action of** flattening out a globe's surface, mapmakers have introduced some errors.

By flattening out a globe's surface, mapmakers have introduced some errors.

21. You can prove this **with the help of** a little experiment. _____

You can prove this by a little experiment.

22. First, **obtain** a paper map of the world and try to make it fit onto a globe. _____

First, buy a paper map of the world and try to make it fit onto a globe.

23. You can accomplish this only **through the action of** folding or cutting the map at the top and bottom.

You can accomplish this only by folding or cutting the map at the top and bottom.

24. Other types of maps have been created **through the actions of** mapmakers. _____

Other types of maps have been created by mapmakers.

25. For instance, you can now **pay for** maps that show all the countries in their correct proportions.

For instance, you can now buy maps that show all the countries in their correct proportions.

26. When you see Indonesia **next to** Australia, you see how big it really is. _____

When you see Indonesia by Australia, you see how big it really is.

Due, Do, and Dew

Learn

A weather map will show snow but not **dew**.
I will **do** my project on weather.
The finished project is **due** in two weeks.

Which boldfaced word means "expected to arrive"? _____ due _____

Which boldfaced word means "light moisture"? _____ dew _____

Which boldfaced word means "act upon"? _____ do _____

> The words **due, do,** and **dew** sound alike but have different meanings and spellings. *Due* is an adjective that means "owed or expected," "adequate or appropriate," or "expected to arrive or be present." *Do* is a verb that means "perform or carry out." It can also mean "work at," "complete," or "bring forth." The past-tense form of *do* is *did*, and the past participle form is *done*. *Dew* is a noun that means "light moisture." This could be water vapor from the air that condenses on cool surfaces or other light moisture.

Practice

Circle the word in parentheses that correctly completes each sentence.

1. Will you (due/**do**/dew) your project on weather or on climate?

2. First I will (due/**do**/dew) the research to learn the difference.

3. Weather might (due/**do**/dew) something different every day.

4. You might see (due/do/**dew**) in the morning and dry heat in the afternoon.

5. Climate describes long-term weather, such as when a rainy season is (**due**/do/dew) to begin.

6. If you (due/**do**/dew) a comparison of Puerto Rico and the Sahara, you will probably compare climates.

7. In places like Puerto Rico, rain showers are (**due**/do/dew) almost every afternoon during some seasons.

8. In much of Great Britain, early risers see (due/do/**dew**) every morning.

9. There you must (due/**do**/dew) some preparation to avoid wet shoes.

10. My library book on Africa is (**due**/do/dew) back next Wednesday.

Apply

Imagine that you are working on a report about Africa, and a friend asks you these questions. Answer each question with a complete sentence, using your imagination if necessary. Use **due, do,** or **dew** in each answer. **Answers will vary. Possible answers appear below.**

11. Will you write about the Great Rift Valley? _____
    Yes, that's what I'll do my report on.

12. Besides Lake Victoria, what other forms of water are found there? _____
    There's lots of dew there.

13. When must you return your book about Africa? _____
    It's due next Monday.

14. How many pages of your report will be about North Africa? _____
    I think I'll do about five.

15. How rainy is Zaire, which is near the equator? _____
    Actually, there's more dew than rain.

16. How will you learn if East Africa is drier than Central Africa? _____
    I'll probably do a search on the Net.

17. How can you show the differences between countries? _____
    I could do some kind of chart.

18. When will the guest from Africa arrive? _____
    She's due late Friday.

19. What question will you ask that person? _____
    How do you do?

20. Would you prefer an oral or a written report next time? _____
    I'd rather do an oral report.

21. Where will your research come from? _____
    I'll do most of it on the Internet.

22. How will you observe the weather in your home state? _____
    I'll do that on the Net, too.

23. How can you record your observations? _____
    I think graphs will be the easiest way to do it.

Metal and *Medal*

Learn

   a. The picture shows the gold **medal** that my cousin won.

   b. Is the **metal** really gold?

Which sentence, **a.** or **b.**, contains a boldfaced word that describes a hard and often shiny substance

that conducts heat and electricity? _____**b.**_____

Which sentence, **a.** or **b.**, contains a word that describes a kind of award? _____**a.**_____

> The words **metal** and **medal** sound somewhat alike but have different spellings and meanings. *Metal* is a noun that means "a substance, such as copper, iron, or gold, that is usually hard and shiny, that conducts heat and electricity, and can be hammered or formed into different shapes." *Metal* can also be an adjective that means "made of metal." *Medal* is also a noun, but it means "a small, flat piece of metal, many times in the form of a coin with words and images, in honor of a special person, action, or achievement."

Practice

Circle the word in parentheses that correctly completes each sentence. (**1.–10.**)

   Our planet has many different kinds of minerals. A mineral may be a rock, a gemstone, or some kind of (**metal**/medal). The most common (**metal**/medal) is aluminum, which is found throughout the world. However, probably the most desirable (**metal**/medal) in history is gold.

   Gold has many uses. It might be made into a ring, a dental crown, or an athletic (metal/**medal**). Because of its usefulness and beauty, people have always looked for gold. Large deposits have been found in Australia, the United States, and South Africa.

   A man named George Walker discovered a huge gold deposit in South Africa. He should have won a (metal/**medal**) for his discovery. Instead, he sold his claim for just a few dollars. No one knows what happened to him.

   Copper is another (**metal**/medal) with a long history. It was used by ancient people, and it, too, is often found in a pure form. In fact, a lump of copper that weighed 500 tons was found in Minnesota.

   Like gold, copper has many uses. Many coins contain copper, and many types of (metals/**medals**) are molded from it, since it is soft and easy to shape into an award. Because it is such a good conductor of electricity, copper is also used in industry.

   Silver is a (**metal**/medal) that is like gold and copper in some ways. In fact, it lies between them in the periodic table of elements. Like gold, it is highly decorative. You might see it in a necklace, a military (metal/**medal**), or a fancy spoon. Like copper, it is a good conductor of electricity. It is also found in many locations, often as a by-product of the search for some other (**metal**/medal).

Apply

Write a question to go with each answer below. Use **metal** or **medal** in each question you write.

11. Question: _____

    Can you tell me about that medal?

    Answer: It is designed to hang around the winner's neck.

12. Question: _____

    What are some different uses of metals?

    Answer: They use gold to make jewelry and copper to make electronic coatings.

13. Question: _____

    What metal is often found in water?

    Answer: They find mainly gold there.

14. Question: _____

    What are the most common metals used for a medal?

    Answer: It is usually made of gold, silver, or bronze.

15. Question: _____

    Why is gold a good metal for making intricate chains?

    Answer: It is easy to shape into wires.

16. Question: _____

    Did the ancient Egyptians have a favorite metal?

    Answer: The ancient Egyptians often used gold in their jewelry.

17. Question: _____

    Who all gets a medal?

    Answer: Everyone who finishes this marathon will receive one.

18. Question: _____

    What metal is this pin made from?

    Answer: This is actually made from tin and not silver.

19. Question: _____

    Why is metal better than wood for bridges?

    Answer: It does not rot like wood does.

Name _____

Weight and *Wait*

Learn

I had a long **wait** in the doctor's office. My **weight** has not changed very much.

Which boldfaced word means "the amount something weighs"? _____ weight _____

Which boldfaced word means "a period of waiting"? _____ wait _____

> The words **weight** and **wait** sound alike but have different spellings and meanings. *Weight* is a noun that means "the amount that something weighs." It can also mean "burden" or "pressure." *Wait* is usually a verb that means "remain in one place." *Wait* can also be a noun that means "a period of waiting."

Practice

Underline the word in parentheses that correctly completes each sentence.

1. If you (weight/<u>wait</u>) a minute, I will tell you an interesting fact.

2. I once thought that a person's (<u>weight</u>/wait) depended only on diet.

3. That is not true; the average (<u>weight</u>/wait) of people differs depending on location.

4. Arctic hunters may have to (weight/<u>wait</u>) for long periods of time in very cold weather.

5. Since fat insulates them, they need more (<u>weight</u>/wait) than some other people.

6. The (<u>weight</u>/wait) of the average person in Spain is almost 40 pounds lighter than that of an Arctic dweller.

7. In hot climates, like that of Spain, too much (<u>weight</u>/wait) is a disadvantage.

8. I had to (weight/<u>wait</u>) a week for this book, but it explained a great deal.

9. Apparently, a person's (<u>weight</u>/wait) is different on a mountaintop than it is at sea level.

10. I can explain why if you are willing to (weight/<u>wait</u>).

11. Gravity affects a person's (<u>weight</u>/wait), so you weigh less the farther you are from Earth's center.

12. If you (weight/<u>wait</u>) for a week at the equator, the same thing holds true.

13. Your (<u>weight</u>/wait) at the equator is less than it would be at either pole.

14. The next time the coach checks my (<u>weight</u>/wait) before a wrestling match, I will explain this.

15. I think she will laugh, so please (weight/<u>wait</u>) and let me tell her.

Apply

Complete each sentence with your own words. Use **weight** or **wait** correctly in the sentence.

16. If the next plane leaves at noon, _we won't have a long wait._

17. If you continue to eat like that, _you'll gain a lot of weight._

18. In this cold climate, _maybe I should add some weight for padding?_

19. If you want to visit the equator, _check your weight before you go and after you get there._

20. This book is not due until next week, so _you can wait to return it to me._

21. Since my partner is late, _don't wait for us to go in._

22. In very cold climates, _extra weight may have a health value._

23. Because we moved from Denver to Los Angeles, _my weight has gone up._

24. If you are not in a hurry, _why don't you wait for Julie with me._

Petal, Pedal, and *Peddle*

Learn

a. Those feathers look like the <u>petals</u> of a giant flower.
b. That man <u>peddles</u> food to the crowd.
c. The girl has decorated the <u>pedals</u> on her bike.

In which sentence, **a., b.,** or **c.,** does the underlined word mean "to travel about selling things"? __b.__

In which sentence, **a., b.,** or **c.,** does the underlined word mean "levers that are worked by the feet"? __c.__

In which sentence, **a., b.,** or **c.,** does the underlined word mean "part of a flower"? __a.__

> The words **petal, pedal,** and **peddle** almost sound alike but have different spellings and meanings. *Petal* is a noun that means "one of the often brightly colored leaflike parts of a flower's corolla." *Pedal* can be a noun that means "a lever that is worked by one or both feet." *Pedal* is also a verb that means "to use or work pedals." *Peddle* is a verb that means "to travel about selling things."

Practice

Underline the word in parentheses that correctly completes each sentence. (**1.–8.**)

Let's go to the West Indian carnival. We can (petal/<u>pedal</u>/peddle) over to the parade. My sister said that this carnival takes place every Labor Day weekend. I have heard that millions of people come both to watch and to participate.

If you have a license, you can (petal/pedal/<u>peddle</u>) food and souvenirs. People like to buy the pickled fish and coconut milk. That vendor has decorated the food with flower (<u>petals</u>/pedals/peddles) and leaves. We can sample food from Cuba, Puerto Rico, Trinidad, and other places.

The music is particularly nice. You can hear steel bands and all kinds of music. That performer is playing an electric steel drum. When he presses his left foot on either (petal/<u>pedal</u>/peddle), the sound changes.

A similar festival takes place in Toronto during July and August. Although we could not (petal/<u>pedal</u>/peddle) our bikes there, perhaps our families could arrange a trip some time. The costumes there are supposed to be really special. Many dancers wear huge headdresses. I cannot tell if the feathers are supposed to look like flower (<u>petals</u>/pedals/peddles) or if they are designed to make the dancers more eye-catching.

Perhaps some summer we could go there and work. I know that students often (petal/pedal/<u>peddle</u>) souvenirs, such as T-shirts. Since you are a good artist, perhaps you could (petal/<u>pedal</u>/peddle) posters or banners.

Apply

Write a question for each answer. Use **petal, pedal,** or **peddle** in each question you write.

9. Question: Which pedal operates the brakes? _____

_____

Answer: The one on the left operates the brakes.

10. Question: Are these petals? _____

_____

Answer: No, these are actually the sepals of the flower.

11. Question: Isn't that orange pretty against the petals? _____

_____

Answer: Yes, the orange butterfly looks pretty against the white flower.

12. Question: What can the vendors peddle here? _____

_____

Answer: They are allowed to sell only certain items.

13. Question: What would you like to peddle? _____

_____

Answer: I would sell Caribbean foods.

14. Question: Did you pedal over here? _____

_____

Answer: Yes, my bicycle works well now.

15. Question: Can we pedal into the park? _____

_____

Answer: I think we have to travel there on foot.

16. Question: Does it look different when the petals open? _____

_____

Answer: After the flower opens, you will see the color inside.

17. Question: What has Marjorie decided to peddle this year? _____

_____

Answer: She drives an ice-cream truck from town to town.

Dye and *Die*

Learn

Many people light candles when someone **dies**. Carla **dyes** her scarf black as a sign of respect.

Which boldfaced word means "stops living"? _____ dies

Which boldfaced word means "colors something"? _____ dyes

> The words **dye** and **die** sound alike but have different spellings and meanings. *Dye* is a noun that means "a substance used to change the color of something." *Dye* can also be a verb that means "to color something, as with dye." The past-tense form of *dye* is *dyed*. *Die* is a verb that means "to stop living." It can also mean "to come to an end." The past-tense form of *die* is *died*.

Practice

Underline the word in parentheses that correctly completes each sentence.

1. When people anywhere (dye/die), friends and families follow certain customs.

2. In India, a family member takes water from the Ganges River to the person who is about to (dye/die).

3. When people (dye/die) in India, friends bring food and flowers.

4. Lao visitors often bring fruit or sweets to families after people (dye/die).

5. Monks visit after someone (dyes/dies).

6. Saffron may be used to (dye/die) their robes yellow.

7. Only the monks wear yellow; other people (dye/die) their clothes black.

8. People who do not own black clothing could probably (dye/die) some.

9. Guests in Cambodia wear either black or white after someone (dyes/dies).

10. In China, when people who are Buddhists (dye/die), their families may have a solemn parade.

11. When people (dye/die), their pictures may be displayed in open cars.

12. Special offerings of incense and food honor the people who (dyed/died).

13. Someone uses red (dye/die) to color the cloth that holds the offerings.

14. The Hmong avoid red at funerals, so they would not use such a (dye/die).

Apply

Rewrite each sentence, replacing the boldfaced words with **dye, dyed, die,** or **died**.

15. Every culture has special rituals to honor and protect those who **are no longer alive**.

    Every culture has special rituals to honor and protect those who die.

    _____

16. Different Native American tribes follow a variety of customs when people **stop living**.

    Different Native American tribes follow a variety of customs when people die.

    _____

17. Not all people who **have passed away** are buried lying down. _____

    Not all people who die are buried lying down.

18. After medicine men **meet death,** they may be buried sitting upright. _____

    After medicine men die, they may be buried sitting upright.

19. Sometimes Native Americans **cease living** in foreign countries. _____

    Sometimes Native Americans die in foreign countries.

20. If their remains are sent home, the families of those who **left this world** may hold a ceremony.

    If their remains are sent home, the families of those who died may hold a ceremony.

    _____

21. People may bring gifts, such as baskets that have been **colored**. _____

    People may bring gifts, such as baskets that have been dyed.

22. Native Americans use a variety of materials to **change the color of** the fibers they use.

    Native Americans use a variety of materials to dye the fibers they use.

    _____

23. One common **coloring substance** is made from yucca roots. _____

    One common dye is made from yucca roots.

24. Because people continue to **arrive at the end of life**, new traditions keep developing.

    Because people continue to die, new traditions keep developing.

    _____

25. In 1997, several people who **passed on** had their remains sent into outer space. _____

    In 1997, several people who died had their remains sent into outer space.

Rain, Reign, and Rein

Learn

a. In whose **reign** was the Great Wall built?

b. Is that horse's **rein** really made of bronze?

c. South China has a lot of **rain**.

Which boldfaced word names a weather condition? _____ rain

Which boldfaced word means "the time when a monarch rules"? _____ reign

Which boldfaced word means "a narrow strap used to control an animal"? _____ rein

> The words **rain, reign,** and **rein** sound alike but have different spellings and meanings. *Rain* is a noun that means "water that falls from clouds to the earth." It can also be a verb that means "to fall in drops of water." *Reign* is a noun that means "the rule of a monarch or sovereign" or "the time when a monarch rules." It can also be a verb that means "to rule." *Rein* is a noun that means "a long narrow strap, usually of leather, used by a rider or a driver to control an animal." It is often used in its plural form, *reins*. *Rein* can also be a verb that means "to control as if by a rein."

Practice

Underline the word in parentheses that correctly completes each sentence. (**1.–8.**)

China is a fascinating place to visit. It got its name under the (rain/reign/rein) of Cheng, a third-century ruler. He was the ruler of a small state called Ch'in, but he later took over more kingdoms. Later, he took on a title that identified him as the First Emperor of Ch'in.

Another famous ruler was Qin Huang Ti. His (rain/reign/rein) was important for several reasons. He was the first real ruler of the country. Before him, China was made up of many separate states. Also, during his (rain/reign/rein), he had artists construct a clay army. This army contains more than 7,000 figures, including chariots, life-sized soldiers of different ranks, and animals. The detail is incredible. Soldiers have laces on their shoes, and the horses have actual (rains/reigns/reins).

The country has many distinct areas. By and large, the weather is cold in the northern areas and warm in the southern areas. In the south, (rain/reign/rein) may fall every day in March, April, and May. Adventurous travelers will want to visit Hohhot, which is in Inner Mongolia. The horseback rider in my picture, who is holding the (rain/reign/rein) in one hand, is from that area. While southern China can be wet at this time of year, visitors to Hohhot may have more trouble with sand than with (rain/reign/rein). This is a place where people often sleep in yurts, which are moveable houses made of skins or cloth. If you want to ride here, you might be handed the (rains/reigns/reins) of a horse or a camel. Many visitors want to have their pictures taken atop a camel.

Apply

Write a question for each answer. Use **rain, reign,** or **rein(s)** in each question you write.

9. Question: _Was the Great Wall begun in the reign of the Emperor Qin Huang Ti?_ _____

_____

Answer: Yes, the Great Wall was begun by the Emperor Qin Huang Ti.

10. Question: _When did Qin reign?_ _____

_____

Answer: He was an early ruler during the Qin Dynasty.

11. Question: _Will it rain when we take our trip?_ _____

_____

Answer: Bring an umbrella if you travel in March.

12. Question: _Do you really expect rain that late?_ _____

_____

Answer: Yes, the weather is still wet in May.

13. Question: _Does it rain a lot?_ _____

_____

Answer: Yes, it falls every day during the rainy season.

14. Question: _Where you able to save the reins?_ _____

_____

Answer: Just one of them was damaged in the fire.

15. Question: _Where did you get the new reins?_ _____

_____

Answer: I went to the harness maker to get them.

16. Question: _How do you hold the reins?_ _____

_____

Answer: An expert rider will hold them both in one hand.

17. Question: _When and where did Elizabeth I reign?_ _____

_____

Answer: Elizabeth I ruled England from 1558 to 1603.

Negatives

Learn

a. My little sister don't have no front teeth anymore.

b. Although she doesn't really believe in the tooth fairy, she won't say this out loud.

Which sentence, **a.** or **b.,** uses too many negative words? ___a.___

Which sentence, **a.** or **b.,** uses negatives correctly? ___b.___

> A **negative** is a word that means "no" or "not." The words *no, not, nothing, none, never, nowhere,* and *nobody* are negatives. The negative word *not* is found in contractions such as *don't* and *wasn't.* Use only one negative in a sentence to express a negative idea. Use the contraction ***doesn't*** with singular subjects, including *he, she,* and *it.* Use the contraction ***don't*** with plural subjects, including *we* and *they.* Use *don't* with *I* and *you,* too.

Practice

Underline the word in parentheses that correctly completes each sentence.

1. Nobody had (ever/never) told me about the magic mouse who trades children's teeth for money.

2. You don't know (nothing/anything) about him either?

3. Many Mexican children don't believe in (any/no) tooth fairy.

4. Nobody in Mexico needs (no/a) tooth fairy, because they have El Raton.

5. Although El Raton (doesn't/don't) look like an English tooth fairy, he acts the same way.

6. Mexican children don't leave their teeth (nowhere/anywhere) on their beds.

7. El Raton wouldn't be able to find (any/no) teeth there, so teeth go into a small box by the bed.

8. Some other countries have a magic rat, but nobody uses (any/no) box.

9. People in Haiti throw a tooth up on the roof, but they (don't/don't never) get money.

10. A child in Oman throws a tooth at the sun and hopes the sun will send (a/no) new one.

11. A German child usually (don't/doesn't) do anything with an old tooth.

12. In Pakistan, if there (is/isn't) no river nearby, a child will throw a tooth into a garden.

13. I (don't/doesn't) know how these customs started.

14. In a few countries, you (will/won't) never find a single custom that everyone follows.

Apply

Write a word from the Word Bank to complete each sentence. Capitalize a word that begins a sentence. Some sentences have more than one correct answer.

Word Bank

not	never	don't	anything
doesn't	no	nothing	any

15. I had _____ no _____ idea that people had so many traditions having to do with teeth!

16. Most people don't see _____ anything _____ odd about their own traditions.

17. _____ Doesn't _____ anyone know what children do in Sweden?

18. There is _____ no _____ tooth fairy in Russia, we learned.

19. _____ Don't _____ children drop their teeth into a hole in the ground?

20. Children in Singapore _____ don't _____ do the same thing with upper and lower teeth.

21. You _____ don't _____ look surprised to learn that they throw their upper teeth up and their lower teeth down.

22. A Malaysian child would _____ not/never _____ throw away any body part, even a tooth.

23. A child in Nepal doesn't want _____ any _____ animal to eat a lost tooth.

24. If an animal ate a lost tooth, a new one would _____ not/never _____ grow in its place.

25. Children in Sri Lanka _____ don't _____ worry about this, since they give their teeth to squirrels.

26. Korean children tell birds that they do _____ not _____ want their old teeth anymore.

27. They want new ones, since they have _____ no _____ need for the old ones.

28. I expect I'll get _____ nothing _____ for the teeth I lose when I grow up.

Lie and *Lay*, *Set* and *Sit*

Learn

Here, you can **sit** next to me.
Tina **set** a pair of chopsticks on the table.

Before eating, I **laid** my napkin on my lap.
The cat **lies** next to the door.

Which boldfaced word means "move your body into a chair"? ____sit____

Which boldfaced word means "recline"? ____lies____ .

Which two boldfaced words mean "place or put something somewhere"? ____set____   ____laid____

> **Lie** and **lay** are different verbs. *Lay* takes a direct object and *lie* does not. *Lie* means "to recline." *Lay* means "to put something down somewhere." The past-tense form of *lie* is *lay*, and the past participle form (the form used with *have*) of *lie* is *lain*. The past-tense form of *lay* is *laid*, and the past participle form of lay is also *laid*. **Set** and **sit** are different verbs. *Set* takes a direct object and *sit* does not. If you're about to use *set*, ask yourself, "Set what?" If you can't answer that question, use *sit*. Also, remember that you can't *sit* anything down—you must *set* it down. The past-tense form of *sit* is *sat*, and the past participle form is also *sat*. *Set* is one of the few verbs that does not change in past or past participle form.

Practice

Circle the word in parentheses that correctly completes each sentence.

1. Let's go out to eat, since we have (laid/**lain**) around all afternoon.

2. Before we choose a restaurant, (**sit**/set) down and watch this show about eating customs.

3. In some Arabic countries, no eating utensils are (**laid**/lain) on the table.

4. The food is (**set**/sat) down, and guests feed themselves with their fingers.

5. Tina, your pet cat has (laid/**lain**) in that spot all day!

6. At Asian meals, people have (sat/**set**) chopsticks in front of me.

7. Unless you (**set**/sit) down a completely empty glass, it will not be refilled.

8. When you finish eating with chopsticks, don't (sit/**set**) them on the table.

9. Notice how those have been (lain/**laid**) across the top of the dish.

10. If you are eating with a Muslim or a Jewish friend, do not (sit/**set**) pork on their plates.

11. Also, if you are (**sitting**/setting) at a table with Navajos, do not expect them to eat fish.

Apply

Rewrite each sentence using a form of *lie, lay, set,* or *sit.* There may be more than one way to rewrite each sentence.   **Answers may vary. Possible answers appear below.**

12. Lek invited me to take a seat next to him. _____
     Lek invited me to sit next to him.

13. The food servers have put knives and forks on the table. _____
     The food servers have set knives and forks on the table.

14. In most Asian restaurants that I visited, chopsticks were placed on the table.
     In most Asian restaurants that I visited, chopsticks were set on the table.

15. Lek explained that we were seated in a Thai restaurant. _____
     Lek explained that we were sitting in a Thai restaurant.

16. People there seldom place chopsticks on the table. _____
     People there seldom (set/lay) chopsticks on the table.

17. In many restaurants, people put all the food on the table at once. _____
     In many restaurants, people (lay/set) all the food on the table at once.

18. In some countries, such as El Salvador, food is placed on each person's plate.
     In some countries, such as El Salvador, food is laid on each person's plate.

19. The plate is put down in front of the person. _____
     The plate is set down in front of the person.

20. We took seats here almost an hour ago. _____
     We sat here almost an hour ago.

21. I am full, and I'm hoping that I can recline somewhere for a few minutes. _____
     I am full, and I'm hoping that I can lie down somewhere for a few minutes.

22. In many countries, you show you're done eating by placing your knife and your fork so the tips rest in the middle of your plate.
     In many countries, you show you're done eating by (laying/setting) your knife and your fork so the tips

     (lie/sit) in the middle of your plate.   [Only one word must be replaced.]

Irregular Verbs

Learn

In the 1900s, ocean mappers **begun** to study the ocean floor. They discovered secrets that had **lain** hidden for years.

Which boldfaced word is an incorrect verb form? _____ *begun*

Many verbs are **irregular;** they do not add *-ed* in the past tense. Here are some of those verbs:

Verb		Past Tense		Past Tense with *has, have,* or *had*	
hold	bring	held	brought	held	brought
build	lie	built	lay	built	lain
sing	lay	sang	laid	sung	laid

Practice

Underline the verb form in parentheses that correctly completes each sentence.

1. For centuries, people (knowed/knew) little about the ocean's depths.

2. Because of the enormous water pressure, no one had (went/gone) to the deepest parts.

3. Now scientists have (tooken/taken) a look at some of the wonders in the ocean.

4. People once (thinked/thought) that the ocean floor was a flat, gentle slope.

5. Then new electronic equipment (came/comed) along.

6. Scientists have now (saw/seen) large portions of the ocean's floor.

7. Those scientists discovered that part of the floor had (lain/laid) flat.

8. Other parts, though, (rose/risen) and fell in steep mountains and trenches.

9. In some places, landmasses just (falled/fell) into deep trenches.

10. Scientists have (began/begun) measuring the ocean's actual depths.

11. I have (did/done) some research, and I discovered that the Arctic Ocean is the shallowest.

12. I have (chose/chosen) to learn more about the Mariana Trench.

13. During the last century, divers have (brung/brought) up some wonderful treasures from the ocean's floor.

14. I (saw/seen) some gold bars that were found in 1981.

Rewrite each sentence, replacing each boldfaced verb with its past-tense form.

15. I **see** pictures of hot springs. _____

I saw the pictures of hot springs.

16. These **lie** deep in the ocean. _____

These lay deep in the ocean.

17. The water **rises** up at temperatures of 600 degrees. _____

The water rose up at temperatures of 600 degrees.

18. I **know** these occurred at edges of the earth's crust. _____

I knew these occurred at edges of the earth's crust.

19. The crust **breaks** apart in places, forming deep cracks. _____

The crust broke apart in places, forming deep cracks.

20. Icy water **falls** into the cracks. _____

Icy water fell into the cracks.

21. It **comes** into contact with hot magma. _____

It came into contact with hot magma.

22. The magma **gives** its heat to the water. _____

The magma gave its heat to the water.

23. The water **grows** extremely hot. _____

The water grew extremely hot.

24. It **brings** minerals from the earth's crust with it. _____

It brought minerals from the earth's crust with it.

25. I'd guess the water **stinks** as a result. _____

I'd guess the water stank as a result.

26. I wonder if something **shrinks** when the magma **expands**. _____

I wonder if something shrank when the magma expanded.

Copyright © Zaner-Bloser, Inc.

Subject Pronouns and Object Pronouns

Learn

Hillary has read "The Legend of Sleepy Hollow." **She** will give a report on **it** next week.

Which boldfaced word replaces the word "Hillary"? _____ She _____

Which boldfaced word replaces "The Legend of Sleepy Hollow"? _____ it _____

> **Subject pronouns** include *I, he, she, we,* and *they*. Subject pronouns can be the subject of a clause or sentence. **Object pronouns** can be used after an action verb or a preposition. Object pronouns include *me, him, her, us,* and *them*. The pronouns *it* and *you* can be either subjects or objects.

Practice

Underline each subject pronoun. Circle each object pronoun.

1. The librarian gave Amy and me a book on early American literature.

2. It told about the life and work of several early writers.

3. I really enjoyed the part about Benjamin Franklin.

4. The book told how he ran away from home when he was just 17.

5. A printer in Philadelphia gave him a job.

6. Amy got a copy of Franklin's *Autobiography*, and she plans to read it this summer.

7. Franklin had many rules for a successful life, and you will recognize many of them.

8. They are simple ones like "A penny saved is a penny earned."

9. Washington Irving's tales are familiar to most of us.

10. Amy and I have a copy of Irving's "Rip Van Winkle," but we also want to read "The Legend of Sleepy Hollow."

11. Irving's popular tales made him the first important American writer.

12. The many novels of James Fenimore Cooper made him very popular in both America and Europe.

13. Cooper came from an aristocratic family, but he set his stories in the frontier.

14. They often featured a hero named Natty Bumppo, a courageous and skillful pioneer.

15. This made him the ideal American.

Rewrite each sentence. Replace each boldfaced phrase with a subject pronoun or an object pronoun.

16. **Emily Dickinson** is one of America's finest poets. _____

    She is one of America's finest poets.

    _____

17. **Emily, her brother Austin, and her sister Lavinia** lived in Amherst, Massachusetts.

    They lived in Amherst, Massachusetts.

    _____

    _____

18. Emily's father, a well-respected lawyer, sent **Emily** to Amherst Academy and Mount Holyoke
    Female Seminary to be educated.

    Emily's father, a well-respected lawyer, sent her to Amherst Academy and Mount Holyoke Female

    Seminary to be educated.

    _____

19. She wrote many poems, but fewer than a dozen of **the poems** were published in her lifetime.

    She wrote many poems, but fewer than a dozen of them were published in her lifetime.

    _____

    _____

20. After Emily met Charles Wadsworth, a married minister, some scholars say she fell hopelessly
    in love with **the Reverend Mr. Wadsworth**.

    After Emily met Charles Wadsworth, a married minister, some scholars say she fell hopelessly in love with him.

    _____

    _____

21. After that, **Emily Dickinson** spent the rest of her life quietly writing short, highly compact poems.

    After that, she spent the rest of her life quietly writing short, highly compact poems.

    _____

    _____

22. Few ever saw **Emily Dickinson** outside of her home. _____

    Few ever saw her outside of her home.

    _____

23. After her death, **Lavinia** found her many unpublished poems. _____

    After her death, she found her many unpublished poems.

    _____

24. **The poems** were published in various collections from 1890 to 1935. _____

    They were published in various collections from 1890 to 1935.

    _____

25. It was only in 1955 that all of **the poems** were finally published.

    It was only in 1955 that all of them were finally published.

    _____

    _____

Compound Subject and Compound Object Pronouns

Learn

a. Tony and I enjoy fantasy stories.
b. A classmate told Tony and I to look for stories by Ray Bradbury.

If you delete "Tony and" from each sentence, which sentence, **a.** or **b.,** sounds correct? **a.**

> Use a **subject pronoun** in a compound subject. Use an **object pronoun** in a compound direct object, a compound indirect object, or a compound object of a preposition. If you are unsure which pronoun form to use, say the sentence with only the pronoun part of the compound. For example: *He told Tony and I.* becomes *He told I.* You can hear that *I* should be replaced with *me.*

Practice

Underline the correct pronoun in each pair.

1. On Saturday, Lisa, Tony, and (I/me) stopped by the library.
2. Our teacher wanted Tony and (I/me) to do some research.
3. We enjoy fantasy, so (he/him) and (I/me) chose Ray Bradbury and Isaac Asimov.
4. Surprisingly, Asimov and (he/him) have quite a bit in common.
5. I enjoy stories by both Asimov and (he/him), but Bradbury's stories are my favorites.
6. When Asimov and (he/him) write stories, they have great plots.
7. But when readers compare Asimov and (he/him), they see some differences.
8. Although both men wrote many stories, Tony and (I/me) think that Asimov wrote more.
9. Both Tony and (I/me) think that Bradbury's settings are memorable.
10. Bradbury's descriptions appeal to Tony and (I/me) because they contain such vivid details.
11. A great many collections have stories by both Asimov and (he/him).
12. The librarian told Lisa and (I/me) that Bradbury considered most of his work fantasy.
13. *The Martian Chronicles* surprised both Lisa and (I/me).
14. Even though it took place on Mars, both Tony, Lisa, and (I/me) thought it was only about humans.
15. Lisa and (he/him) think Bradbury's characters are very true to life.

Apply

Rewrite each sentence. Add one or more subject or object pronouns to complete the sentence.

16. My parents encourage my sister, my brother, and _____ to read. _____

My parents encourage my sister, my brother, and me to read.

17. My brother and _____ both read <u>Dandelion Wine</u>. _____

My brother and I/she both read <u>Dandelion Wine</u>.

18. Everyone thought that _____ and _____ would enjoy it. _____

Everyone thought that he/she/I and he/she/I would enjoy it.

19. The story had a different meaning to _____ and _____. _____

The story had a different meaning to him/her/me and him/her/me.

20. Bradbury and _____ both grew up in towns in the Midwest. _____ and _____ have similar backgrounds.

Bradbury and I both grew up in towns in the Midwest. He and I have similar backgrounds.

21. The stories could have been about both Bradbury and _____. _____

The stories could have been about both Bradbury and me.

22. Last month both my brother and _____ heard a recording. _____

Last month both my brother and I heard a recording.

23. Bradbury read some stories aloud to _____ and _____. _____

Bradbury read some stories aloud to him and me.

24. His voice captured our interest. _____ read well! _____

His voice captured our interest. He read well!

25. On long trips, my parents and _____ often listen to books on tape. _____

On long trips, my parents and we often listen to books on tape.

26. Everyone selects one, and _____ chose the one by Bradbury. _____

Everyone selects one, and I chose the one by Bradbury.

27. Of all of _____, his selection was enjoyed most by _____. _____

Of all of us, his selection was enjoyed most by me.

28. Two of my favorites are by Asimov and _____. _____

Two of my favorites are by Asimov and him.

Pronoun Antecedents

Learn

My friend Jess lives in the Northwest. **She** knows many Native American folktales.

What proper noun is replaced by the boldfaced pronoun? _____Jess_____

> An **antecedent** is the word or phrase a pronoun refers to or takes the place of. The antecedent always includes a noun. When you write a pronoun, be sure its antecedent is clear. A pronoun must also **agree** with its antecedent. An antecedent and pronoun agree when they have the same number (singular or plural) and gender (male or female). For example, *women,* a plural noun naming females, would never be the antecedent of *he,* a singular masculine pronoun.

Practice

Underline the antecedent of each boldfaced pronoun.

1. Many native tribes tell traditional stories about Raven. **He** is a complex character.

2. Tribal stories are important. **They** pass on a tribe's beliefs and values.

3. Jess, a friend from Seattle, knows many traditional stories. **She** explained that many feature animals.

4. The animals, however, are often supernatural. **They** can change their form.

5. Some animals in the stories are clever and mischievous. People often call **them** tricksters.

6. In the Great Plains, Coyote is a popular trickster. **He** can be both foolish and bold.

7. Jess knows many native people around Seattle, Washington. **They** tell stories about a different trickster, Raven.

8. One story tells about the beginnings of the world. **It** explains where fire came from.

9. Humans feared the winter ahead. Unlike Raven, **they** had no feathers that would keep them warm.

10. Qok kept fire in a faraway place. He did not want to share **it** with humans.

11. Raven tricked Qok and managed to steal the fire from **him**.

12. Raven and a friend, Jay, brought the fire to Earth. **They** showed humans how to use it.

13. Fire can be dangerous, so Raven showed people how to control **it**.

14. In other stories, Raven has different qualities. For example, in some **he** is a creator.

15. An actual raven is a large bird. **It** is a relative of the crow.

Apply

Write a sentence that might follow each sentence below. Use pronouns to replace the boldfaced nouns.

16. **Raven** is a black raven and **Qok** is a white snowy owl. _____
    They were in competition with each other.

17. **Raven** changed his shape. _____
    He became other animals.

18. In one story, **Raven** had a **twin**. _____
    His twin/She envied him.

19. Raven once helped **people who fish**. _____
    They were very thankful.

20. Raven fell in love with **a beautiful young female goose**. _____
    She wasn't sure she cared for him.

21. **The goose family** liked Raven. _____
    They thought he was clever.

22. However, Raven had trouble crossing **the Clapping Mountains**. _____
    They had a strange power over him.

23. **My parents and I** saw a carving of Raven. _____
    We wondered how old it was.

24. **Native Americans** live throughout North America. _____
    Only some of them tell about Raven.

25. **A story about Raven** will probably come from the Northwest. _____
    It is a traditional tale.

26. **Anansi the Spider** is a popular African American trickster. _____
    He can be really stupid though.

27. Anansi gets credit for **bringing stories to the people**. _____
    That's the best thing he ever did.

28. Could we make up a story about **all three tricksters** together? _____
    They could try to outwit one another.

Using *Who* or *Whom*

Learn

Many flowers are named for the people **who** discovered them.
I asked for **whom** the fuchsia was named.

Which boldfaced word is the subject of a clause? _____who_____

Which boldfaced word is the object of a preposition? _____whom_____

> Use **who** as the **subject** of a sentence or a clause. Use **whom** as the **object** of a verb or a preposition.

Practice

Underline the pronoun in parentheses to complete each sentence correctly.

1. I have neighbors (who/whom) work in the garden every chance they get.

2. To (who/whom) are you referring?

3. I mean the family (who/whom) lives down the street.

4. They told me about Dr. Leonhard Fuchs, (who/whom) wrote a book about plants.

5. He is a man (who/whom) few people remember, except for his name.

6. (Who/Whom) actually named the flower?

7. A monk named Charles Plumier, (who/whom) also named the begonia, the lobelia, and the magnolia.

8. He named these for other botanists for (who/whom) he had respect.

9. Another interesting botanist was William Forsyth, for (who/whom) forsythia is named.

10. What does that plant look like? (Who/Whom) has one?

11. Forsyth, (who/whom) wound up in trouble, brought the plant from China.

12. He was a man (who/whom) an expert had accused of selling a worthless plant medicine.

13. Can you tell me for (who/whom) the jonquil is named?

14. My friend Rosa, from (who/whom) I learned Spanish, explained that its name comes from a Spanish word, *junquillo*.

15. I've always wondered (who/whom) names plants.

Apply

Write a question to go with each answer. Use **who** or **whom** in your question. Be sure to end each question with a question mark.

16. Question: Who named the wisteria? _____

_____

Answer: Thomas Nuttall coined the term *wisteria* to name a climbing shrub.

17. Question: Who did he name it for?/For whom did he name it? _____

_____

Answer: He named the plant for Dr. Caspar Wistar.

18. Question: Who was Dr. Wistar? _____

Answer: Dr. Wistar was an American anatomist who died in 1818.

19. Question: Who designed our plant classifications? _____

_____

Answer: Linnaeus suggested a new way to classify all plants.

20. Question: For whom was sweet william named? _____

_____

Answer: No one knows for certain how the sweet william got its name.

21. Question: For whom were sunflowers named? _____

_____

Answer: The sunflower, or helianthus, is named after the mythological character Helios.

22. Question: Who was he? _____

Answer: Helios was the Greek sun god.

23. Question: Who named the black-eyed Susan? _____

_____

Answer: No one is sure who first called the rudbeckia a black-eyed Susan.

24. Question: Who was the poinsettia named for? _____

_____

Answer: Dr. Joel Roberts Poinsett was a U.S. minister to Mexico in the 1820s.

25. Question: About whom will you do your report? _____

_____

Answer: I have been reading about Dr. Poinsett and the flower named for him.

Making Subject and Verb Agree

Learn

The **words** in our **dictionary** come from many sources.

What boldfaced noun is the simple subject of this sentence? _____words_____ Is this noun

singular or plural? _____plural_____ Underline the verb that agrees with the subject. What form

of this verb would be used if the simple subject of this sentence was *word*? _____comes_____

> The **subject** and its **verb must agree**. Add *-s* or *-es* to a regular verb in the present tense when the subject is a singular noun or *he, she,* or *it*. Do not add *-s* or *-es* to a regular verb in the present tense when the subject is a plural noun or *I, you, we,* or *they*. Some verbs have irregular forms. Singular forms of *be* are *am, is, was*. Plural forms are *are* and *were*. Be sure the verb agrees with its subject and not with the object of a preposition that comes before the verb.

Practice

Underline the simple subject in each sentence. Then circle the correct form of the verb in parentheses.

1. Some people in my family (is/**are**) collectors of facts about words.
2. The origin of some words (**is**/are) foreign.
3. Some of them (**come**/comes) from Spanish, Latin, or Native American languages.
4. A rope for catching cattle (**is**/are) called a lariat, which comes from the Spanish words *la reata*.
5. The name for pink flamingoes (come/**comes**) from the Latin *flamma*, which means "flame."
6. That animal with black and white stripes (get/**gets**) its name, *skunk*, from an Algonquian word.
7. Many words in English (**come**/comes) from the name of a particular place.
8. The hamburgers on your table (is/**are**) named for Hamburg, a city in Germany.
9. Words used in England (is/**are**) sometimes different in meaning from the same words in the United States.
10. In the United States, a person with many bonnets (own/**owns**) several hats.
11. People in England with many bonnets (**own**/owns) car parts.
12. Public schools in England (is/**are**) called private schools in the United States.
13. The gasoline in cars (**is**/are) called petrol in England.

Underline the simple subject in each sentence. Then rewrite the sentence adding the correct form of the verb in parentheses to complete the sentence.

14. The <u>sounds</u> of water (be) reflected in many words. _____

The sounds of water are reflected in many words.

15. The <u>name</u> for alligators (have) been formed from the Spanish word for lizard.

The name for alligators has been formed from the Spanish word for lizard.

16. The Greek <u>words</u> that mean nose and horn, *rhinos* and *keras*, (be) the origin of the word *rhinoceros*.

The Greek words that mean nose and horn, *rhinos* and *keras*, are the origin of the word *rhinoceros*.

17. <u>People</u> in ancient Rome (be) worshipping a goddess named Ceres, whose name was the basis for *cereal*.

People in ancient Rome were worshipping a goddess named Ceres, whose name was the basis for *cereal*.

18. Two <u>words</u> in Dutch, *kool* and *sla*, (be) the basis for our word *coleslaw*. _____

Two words in Dutch, *kool* and *sla*, are the basis for our word *coleslaw*.

19. <u>People</u> who wear denim (be) often unaware of the word's origins. _____

People who wear denim are often unaware of the word's origins.

20. <u>Workers</u> in Nîmes, France, (be) known for the cloth that they made. _____

Workers in Nîmes, France, were known for the cloth that they made.

21. <u>Pairs</u> of words (have) often been joined to make new compound words. _____

Pairs of words have often been joined to make new compound words.

22. A <u>book</u> about word origins often (use) the word *motel* as an example. _____

A book about word origins often uses the word *motel* as an example.

23. A <u>person</u> in a hurry (say) *motel* faster than *motor hotel*. _____

A person in a hurry says *motel* faster than *motor hotel*.

24. <u>Ohm</u> and *ampere* (repeat) the names of physicists. _____

Ohm and *ampere* repeat the names of physicists.

Copyright © Zaner-Bloser, Inc.

Agreement With Compound Subjects

Learn

a. Neither the spectators nor the hare (expects) the tortoise to win.
b. The tortoise and the hare (start) the race.

Underline the compound subject in each sentence. Circle the verb in each sentence.

Which sentence, **a.** or **b.**, has a verb that goes with a singular subject? ___a.___

> A **compound subject** and its verb must agree. If a compound subject includes the conjunction *and,* the subject is plural and needs a plural verb. If a compound subject includes *or* or *nor,* the verb must agree with the closest item in the subject.

Practice

Look at the compound subject in each sentence. Circle the conjunction. Then underline the correct verb in parentheses.

1. The Indians, Greeks, (and) Persians (tell/tells) many fables.

2. Neither the Persians (nor) the storyteller Aesop (are/is) the creator of this form of narrative.

3. A fable (and) a parable (are/is) alike in many ways.

4. Folktales, fables, (and) parables (is/are) all short stories.

5. Their purpose (and) form (are/is) often similar.

6. An animal, a human, (or) an object (are/is) often the main character in a fable.

7. Lions, foolish people, (and) even a pot (are/is) characters in fables by Aesop.

8. A foolish character (and) a greedy one (appear/appears) frequently.

9. The characters' actions (and) the results of those actions (teaches/teach) a lesson.

10. Either rewards (or) some punishment (follow/follows) a decision.

11. Many adults (and) children (enjoy/enjoys) the fables of Aesop.

12. Neither our teacher (nor) other experts (know/knows) if Aesop was real.

13. Nevertheless, the grasshopper (and) the ant (delights/delight) readers.

14. The Indians (and) the Greeks (is/are) not the only people with fables.

15. Russians, Africans, Chinese, (and) others (tells/tell) fables, too.

Rewrite each sentence. Add a verb in the present tense to complete the sentence.

16. A tortoise and a family of hares _____ on a road one day. _____`
A tortoise and a family of hares are on a road one day.
_____

17. Either the hares or the tortoise _____ talking about a race. _____
Either the hares or the tortoise is talking about a race.
_____

18. A young hare and an older one _____ making fun of the tortoise. _____
A young hare and an older one are making fun of the tortoise.
_____

19. Neither the tortoise nor his friends _____ paying attention at first. _____
Neither the tortoise nor his friends are paying attention at first.
_____

20. However, the friends and the tortoise _____ tired of all the jokes. _____
However, the friends and the tortoise are getting tired of all the jokes.
_____

21. Either the tortoise or the hares _____ a race. _____
Either the tortoise or the hares propose a race.
_____

22. The hare and the other animals _____ at the idea. _____
The hare and the other animals laugh at the idea.
_____

23. After all, a tortoise and a snail _____ very slowly. _____
After all, a tortoise and a snail move very slowly.
_____

24. Still, the tortoise and the hare _____ to race. _____
Still, the tortoise and the hare agree to race.
_____

25. Neither the tortoise nor the hares _____ what actually happened. _____
Neither the tortoise nor the hares know what actually happened.
_____

26. At first, both the tortoise and the hare _____ running as hard as possible. _____
At first both the tortoise and the hare are running as hard as possible.
_____

27. Either the hare or the hare's friends _____ why the hare took a nap. _____
Either the hare or the hare's friends know why the hare took a nap.
_____

28. Adults and children _____ the moral: slow and steady wins the race. _____
Adults and children know the moral: slow and steady wins the race.
_____

Making Subject and Verb Agree: Special Cases

Learn

My reading group meets every Monday. This week, **Julie of the Wolves** is being discussed. **Everyone** has an opinion about it.

The subjects of these sentences are shown in boldface type. Do the verbs that follow these

subjects agree with singular subjects or with plural subjects? _____singular_____

> The **subject** and its **verb must agree**. There are special rules for certain kinds of subjects. **Titles** of books, movies, stories, or songs are considered singular even if they end in -s. ("The Three Little Pigs" is my brother's favorite story.) A **collective noun,** such as collection, group, team, country, kingdom, family, flock, and herd, names more than one person or object acting together as one group. These nouns are almost always considered singular. (Katie's <u>team</u> wins every game.) Many **indefinite pronouns,** including everyone, nobody, nothing, something, and any-thing, are considered singular. (<u>Everyone</u> likes pizza.) A few indefinite pronouns, such as many and several, are considered plural. (<u>Many</u> like spaghetti.)

Practice

Circle the simple subject in each sentence. Then underline the correct form of each verb in parentheses.

1. *Julie of the Wolves* (is/are) only one of Jean Craighead George's books.

2. Among my friends, nobody (has/have) been to the Alaskan tundra.

3. Everyone (agrees/agree) that this book gives them a feeling for Alaska.

4. The author's family (were/was) filled with naturalists, and her books reflect this.

5. For example, *Water Sky* (is/are) a book about whales.

6. A group of Eskimos (were/was) very helpful to the writer, since they were studying the whales.

7. A scientific team (was/were) counting whales and invited George along.

8. A collection of George's books (include/includes) dozens of titles.

9. Besides *Julie of the Wolves,* several (has/have) animal names in the titles.

10. *Snow Tracks* (is/are) one of George's oldest titles, published in 1958.

11. At George's home, something (help/helps) her write.

Apply

Follow the directions to write a sentence. Use the boldfaced word or words in the sentence you write. Include a verb that requires you to choose between the singular and the plural form.

12. Describe something that a **pack of wolves** might do. _____

A pack of wolves is a magnificent sight.

_____

13. Name an animal that **nobody** would keep as a pet. _____

Nobody I know keeps a cockroach as a pet.

_____

14. Tell what the book <u>**River Rats**</u> may be about. _____

<u>River Rats</u> is probably about some boys who hang around a river.

_____

15. Imagine you see a **flock** of birds. Describe the flock's actions. _____

The flock moves in a pattern.

_____

16. Compare a **school** of fish with a **pod** of whales. _____

A school of fish is smaller than a pod of whales.

_____

17. Describe a place where a **pride** of lions might live. _____

A pride of lions rules this part of Kruger National Park.

_____

18. Guess one animal that is likely to be in **Julie of the Wolves**. _____

More than one wolf has to be part of <u>Julie of the Wolves</u>.

_____

19. Explain why one wolf would be less dangerous than **several**. _____

Several are more likely to gang up on you.   [preferably not "several wolves"]

_____

20. Identify a place where **someone** could probably see wildlife. _____

If someone walks into the woods, he or she should see wildlife.

_____

21. Tell one **country** you would use as the setting for a novel and why. _____

My favorite country is Brazil, so I'd set my novel there.

_____

22. State your opinion of **"Hansel and Gretel."** _____

"Hansel and Gretel" is a baby story!

_____

Avoiding Dangling Modifiers

Learn

a. Needing to understand a particular symbol, Victoria reached for a dictionary.

b. When searching for the meaning of an unusual symbol, dictionaries are invaluable.

Who needs to understand a symbol in sentence **a.**? _Victoria_____

Does sentence **b.** say exactly who is searching for the meaning of an unusual symbol? _no_____

> Verbal phrases must always refer to, or modify, a noun or a pronoun in the main part of a sentence. **Dangling modifiers** are phrases that do not clearly refer to any particular word in the sentence. Dangling modifiers make your writing unclear, so avoid them in your writing. When you begin a sentence with a verbal phrase, such as "When telling stories to children," make sure that the question "Who is telling?" is answered clearly in the next part of the sentence.

Practice

Underline the verbal phrase that begins each sentence. If the phrase is a dangling modifier, write **DM** on the line. If the phrase is used correctly, circle the word it modifies and write **C** on the line.

1. While reading newspapers, we came across many unfamiliar words, symbols, and abbreviations. ___C___

2. Wanting to understand them, dictionaries were searched. ___DM___

3. Used by the English, the abbreviation P.M. means "Prime Minister." ___C___

4. Seeing the same abbreviation with hours, it means "post meridiem." ___DM___

5. Written on an envelope, the letters CA stand for the state of California. ___C___

6. When used with periods by an accountant, there is quite a different meaning. ___DM___

7. Seeing the word COT, its meaning was unclear to Carlos. ___DM___

8. Written in all capital letters, we learned that COT means "change of temperature." ___DM___

9. Discovered on one page, we found OOD, OOG, OOT, and OOW. ___DM___

10. Trying to pronounce these abbreviations, much laughter followed. ___DM___

11. Inventing a type of dictionary game, Jay began asking questions. ___C___

12. While using a computer, RAM is frequently mentioned. ___DM___

13. Not realizing that RAM stands for "random access memory," Pat thought it was a short word. ___C___

Apply

Rewrite each sentence so the dangling modifier describes the subject of the sentence. You may need to supply the subject and revise the dangling modifier itself. There is more than one way to rewrite each sentence.

14. Writing about proofreading, some symbols were not clear. _____
While writing about proofreading, the teacher didn't make the symbols clear.

15. Knowing a capital letter was needed, three lines were drawn beneath it. _____
Knowing a capital letter was needed, he drew three lines beneath it.

16. Unsure of how to mark boldface type, a visual dictionary was consulted. _____
Unsure of how to mark boldface type, I consulted a visual dictionary.

17. Displayed on a full page, we looked at the proofreading sample. _____
Displayed on a full page, the proofreading sample was very helpful to us.

18. Divided into topics, writers can learn the correct names of familiar items. _____
Divided into topics, correct names of familiar items are more easily learned.

19. Containing labeled pictures, we looked for the pages on communications. _____
Containing labeled pictures, the pages on communications were easy to find.

20. Seeing a dot inside a circle, a period should be inserted. _____
Seeing a dot inside a circle, the writer should insert a period.

21. Wanting a capital letter omitted, the letters "lc" were written. _____
Wanting a capital letter omitted, I wrote the letters "lc."

22. Connecting two words that are typed in the wrong order, a special symbol is used.
For connecting two words that are typed in the wrong order, you use a special symbol.

23. Writing on a computer, italic type can be typed directly. _____
Writing on a computer, I don't mind having to use italic.

24. Using typesetting machines, underlining indicated italic type. _____
Using typesetting machines, people had to show italic by underlining.

25. Printed in all caps, we thought the heading looked good. _____
Printed in all caps, the heading looked good to us.

Comparative and Superlative Modifiers

Learn

In general, poetry is **more concentrated** than prose. Haiku is one of the **most concentrated** forms of poetry.

Underline the boldfaced words that compare poetry with prose. Which boldfaced words compare haiku

with more than one other form of poetry? _____most concentrated_____

> The **comparative form** of an **adjective** or **adverb** compares two people, places,
> things, or actions. Add -er to short adjectives or adverbs to create the comparative
> form. Use the word *more* before long adjectives and adverbs (generally three or
> more syllables) to create the comparative form (*more exaggerated*). The **superlative
> form** compares three or more people, places, things, or actions. Add -est to create
> the superlative form. Use the word *most* before long adjectives and adverbs to
> create the superlative form (*most exaggerated*). Use *better* and *less* to compare two
> things. Use *best* and *least* to compare three or more things.

Practice

Think about how many things are being compared in each sentence. Then underline the correct
form of the adjective or adverb in parentheses.

1. Poems are often the (better/best) way of all that a writer can express feelings.

2. Poems may be long or short; an epic is (longer/longest) than a haiku.

3. An epic is serious, but a limerick is usually (more/most) humorous.

4. One of the (more/most) famous limericks ever is about a young lady from Niger.

5. A haiku, with seventeen syllables, is (shorter/shortest) than a limerick.

6. Often one form of poetry is (better/best) suited to a topic than another form.

7. For example, a poet would be (less/least) likely to use a limerick than a haiku if the subject
   were nature.

8. Poets trying to tell stories are (more/most) likely to write ballads than odes.

9. An elegy is (sadder/saddest) than a limerick, since it deals with someone's death.

10. A name poem is one of the (easier/easiest) kinds of any to write.

11. Many writers find poems (easier/easiest) to write than stories.

12. Today, the (more/most) popular poets of all are probably songwriters.

Apply

Write a question to go with each answer below. Use a comparative or superlative form of an adjective or adverb in each question.

16. Question: Which is longer, a couplet or a triplet?

Answer: A couplet is a two-line stanza, whereas a triplet has three lines.

17. Question: Does a ballad cover less time than an epic?

Answer: The ballad tells a brief story, whereas the epic covers years.

18. Question: Who is better known, Robert Frost or Sara Teasdale?

Answer: The students had heard of Robert Frost but not Sara Teasdale.

19. Question: What is Frost's best-known poem?

Answer: Almost all the students knew "Stopping by Woods on a Snowy Evening."

20. Question: Why are poems easier to remember than paragraphs?

Answer: Rhymes help people remember the lines.

21. Question: What's the most enjoyable thing about poetry?

Answer: Most readers enjoy the descriptive words and images.

22. Question: Is traditional poetry harder or easier to write than free verse?

Answer: Traditional poetry follows a set structure, but free verse does not.

23. Question: Which takes longer to read, a poem or a story?

Answer: Most poems can be read in a few minutes, while a story may take a long time.

24. Question: What is the most beautiful sonnet you've read?

Answer: I cannot decide, since all those sonnets are very beautiful.

Auxiliary Verbs

Learn

Some day, you **might give** a speech. A prepared speaker **will enjoy** public speaking.

Look at the boldfaced verbs. What is the main verb in each sentence?

_____give_____   _____enjoy_____

Underline the auxiliary verb that works with each main verb.

> An **auxiliary verb,** or **helping verb,** works with a main verb. Auxiliary verbs have a variety of purposes. Some auxiliary verbs, such as *can, could, should, might, may,* and *must,* show how likely it is that something will happen. Some auxiliary verbs, such as *did, had, is, will,* and *would,* indicate the tense of the main verb.

Practice

Circle the auxiliary verb or verbs in each sentence.

1. Most people will speak in public at some time in their lives.

2. Some people may try to avoid this out of fear.

3. Everyone should learn the most important tip for public speaking: preparation.

4. First, a good speaker will consider the audience, its interests, and its knowledge.

5. This knowledge can help the speaker in several ways.

6. You will need lively details and anecdotes for most audiences.

7. However, an audience of experts will probably need little background information.

8. A touch of humor would grab the attention of most listeners.

9. You should organize your ideas in some logical way.

10. Otherwise, people in the audience might struggle to understand you.

11. Simple language and clear transitional words can help listeners follow your thinking.

12. A speaker must always speak clearly and at a relaxed speed.

13. You should practice a speech several times in front of a mirror or a friend.

14. Most people in the audience would appreciate visual aids during a long speech.

15. While talking, good speakers may look at individuals in the audience.

Rewrite each sentence, adding an auxiliary verb to each boldfaced verb. There is more than one way to rewrite each sentence. Use as many different auxiliary verbs as you can.

16. Often, speakers **use** audio or visual aids. _____
Often, speakers will use audio or visual aids.

17. Experienced speakers **practice** handling these. _____
Experienced speakers do practice handling these.

18. You **know** how much time your speech takes. _____
You must know how much time your speech takes.

19. You **ask** a friend to time one of your rehearsals. _____
You might ask a friend to time one of your rehearsals.

20. Good speakers **wear** comfortable clothing. _____
Good speakers will wear comfortable clothing.

21. They **arrive** a few minutes early, so they will be calm. _____
They may arrive a few minutes early, so they will be calm.

22. You **look** for one or two friendly faces in the audience. _____
You should look for one or two friendly faces in the audience.

23. Some people in an audience **nod** and smile. _____
Some people in an audience may nod and smile.

24. Large, clear notes **help** a speaker feel confident. _____
Large, clear notes will help a speaker feel confident.

25. You **smile** as you step on stage, because most people **return** a smile. _____
You could smile as you step on stage, because most people will return a smile.

26. You **find** it's better to rehearse standing up. _____
You might find it's better to rehearse standing up.

27. Inexperienced speakers **hesitate** to use gestures. _____
Inexperienced speakers may hesitate to use gestures.

28. Even when using a microphone, you **speak** with a firm voice. _____
Even when using a microphone, you must speak with a firm voice.

Capitalization

Learn

Last week, my uncle and I visited a (museum).
The **Ashmolean Museum** has a famous collection of **Japanese** carvings.

Circle the boldfaced word that names any building where art is displayed.
Underline the boldfaced words that name a specific building of that type.

Which boldfaced word is an adjective? _____ *Japanese* _____

A common noun names a person, place, thing, or idea. A **proper noun** names a specific person, place, thing, or idea. The important words in proper nouns are **capitalized**. **Proper adjectives** are descriptive words formed from proper nouns. They must be capitalized. A **title of respect,** such as *Mr.* or *Judge,* is used before a person's name. This title is also capitalized. The names of the months, the names of the days of the week, and the first word of every sentence are always capitalized.

Practice

Draw three lines (≡) under each lowercase letter that should be a capital letter. Draw a line (/) through each capital letter that should be a lowercase letter.

1. On saturday, uncle arthur invited me out to Lunch.

2. He and i were going to see japanese art at the peabody essex museum.

3. This massachusetts museum was showing a collection of netsuke from asia and other places.

4. Netsuke are small carvings that originated in japan many centuries ago.

5. Today, netsuke are made in many Countries, including england.

6. at first, netsuke were made mainly from chinese ivory or wood.

7. The cities of kyoto and osaka had many well-known artists.

8. While some netsuke show plants or animals, one shows a dutch trader clutching a Rooster.

9. In new york, you can see netsuke at the metropolitan museum of art.

10. My aunt miriam bought my Uncle some books about netsuke.

11. The one that was written by mr. norman sandfield has almost 400 pages.

12. My Uncle bought several netsuke in new orleans last july.

Read the following passage. Then rewrite it with correct capitalization. (**13.–24.**)

Many Artists throughout the world have been influenced by japanese artists. in the 1800s, shops in paris began selling japanese prints. The designs influenced several artists of the time. these included mary cassatt and edgar degas, among others. Cassatt even tried her own hand at print-making. she completed hundreds of prints, many of which have a japanese flavor.

The american architect frank lloyd wright also loved asian art. he was born in wisconsin and built many houses in the united states. however, one of his most famous buildings is in tokyo, japan. he designed the imperial hotel in that city. he owned a very large Collection of japanese prints. several Museums, including the art institute of Chicago, have prints from his Collection.

Many artists throughout the world have been influenced by Japanese artists. In the 1800s,

shops in Paris began selling Japanese prints. The designs influenced several artists of the time.

These included Mary Cassatt and Edgar Degas, among others. Cassatt even tried her own

hand at printmaking. She completed hundreds of prints, many of which have a Japanese

flavor.

The American architect Frank Lloyd Wright also loved Asian art. He was born in Wisconsin

and built many houses in the United States. However, one of his most famous buildings

is in Tokyo, Japan. He designed the Imperial Hotel in that city. He owned a very large

collection of Japanese prints. Several museums, including the Art Institute of Chicago, have

prints from his collection.

Initials and Abbreviations

Dr. Ⓡ. Hsia will give a lecture about Mt. Rushmore
Tues., Jan. 22
Civic Auditorium
112 Southern Ave.

Underline the short way to write *Doctor, Mount, Tuesday,* and *Avenue.*
Circle the letter that stands for a name.

An **abbreviation** is a shortened form of a word. **Titles of respect** are usually abbreviated. So are words in **addresses,** such as *Street* (*St.*), *Avenue* (*Ave.*), and *Boulevard* (*Blvd*). The names of **days,** the names of some **months,** and certain words in the names of **businesses** are often abbreviated in informal notes. These abbreviations begin with a capital letter and end with a period. An **initial** can replace a person's or a place's name. It is written as a capital letter followed by a period.

Practice

Draw three lines (≡) under each lowercase letter that should be a capital letter. Draw a line (/) through each capital letter that should be a lowercase letter. Add periods where they are needed. (**1.–20.**)

Do you know the local business called Memorials, inc? It is located on Main st. It is right near the intersection of Turner ave. The picture on its stationery shows mt. Rushmore. This is one of the most famous Sculptures in the u.s.a. It contains the faces of four u.s. presidents: Washington, Jefferson, Roosevelt, and Lincoln. It shows Theodore Roosevelt, by the way, not f.d.r.

The carving was first proposed by mr. Doane Robinson, a Historian from South Dakota. He had originally suggested western heroes. However, the sculptor was mr. j. Gutzon Borglum, and he disagreed. He thought the work should represent the entire Country, so he chose four Presidents. Ideas for other faces were suggested, including that of Susan b. Anthony, but they were later turned down.

Borglum chose mt. Rushmore because of its hard, fine granite. He worked on the carving for years. However, on mar. 6, 1941 (which was a thurs), he died, just before the Monument was completed. His son, mr. Lincoln Borglum, finished the project. The money to pay for it came from private donations and from Washington, d.c.

Apply

Rewrite each item below, using abbreviations and initials for the boldfaced words where appropriate.

21. drive up **Mount Washington**

    drive up Mt. Washington

22. by Stone **Carvers, Incorporated**

    by Stone Carvers, Inc.

23. across **Sunrise Boulevard**

    across Sunrise Blvd.

24. **Mister John Gutzon Borglum**

    Mr. J. G. Borglum

25. statue of **Saint Francis**

    statue of St. Francis

26. **Martin Styles, Junior**

    Martin Styles, Jr.

27. **General** George **Custer**

    Gen. George Custer

28. **September 5,** 1968

    Sept. 5, 1968

29. born in **the United States of America**

    born in the U.S.A.

30. take the **Skyline Drive**

    take the Skyline Dr.

31. sponsored by the **Durgin Corporation**

    sponsored by the Durgin Corp.

32. **Doctor Rebecca Vann** spoke

    Dr. R. Vann spoke

33. the first house on **Euclid Boulevard**

    the first house on Euclid Blvd.

34. left on **Woodward Street**

    left on Woodward St.

35. **Mistress Hsia** opened the door

    Mrs. Hsia opened the door

36. **next Sunday** afternoon

    next Sun. afternoon

37. at the end of **December**

    at the end of Dec.

38. arrive next **Thursday**

    arrive next Thurs.

39. another house on **Booth Avenue**

    another house on Booth Ave.

40. from **Wednesday to Friday**

    from Wed. to Fri.   [NOT "Wed.–Fri."]

Titles

Learn

Last week we saw a film called (Lust for Life). We also listened to the song "Vincent." Both are about the painter Vincent van Gogh.

Circle the movie title. Underline the song title.

How are they written differently? <u>Lust for Life</u>/The movie title is underlined.

"Vincent"/The song title has quotation marks.

> Underline the **titles** of **books, magazines, newspapers,** and **movies** (or **videos**). These are written in italics in printed text. Use quotation marks around the titles of **songs, stories,** and **poems.** Capitalize the first word and the last word in titles. Capitalize all other words except articles, short prepositions, and coordinating conjunctions. Remember to capitalize short verbs, such as *is* and *are*.

Practice

Draw three lines (≡) under each lowercase letter that should be a capital letter. Underline or add quotation marks to titles. (**1.–10.**)

       Vincent van Gogh was not only a great artist, but also a fascinating person. His life has been the subject of numerous books and films. <u>Lust for life</u> was the first movie that I saw about him. Later, I watched <u>Vincent and Theo</u>, which is about the artist and his brother. Those movies interested me enough to go to the library, where I found the book <u>Van Gogh: The complete paintings</u>. This book showed me some of the paintings that I had not seen before.

       Luckily, my video store had <u>Vincent: The life and death of Vincent van Gogh</u>, so I watched that last week. I learned yesterday that someone has created a fictional film called <u>starry night</u>. It was more or less inspired by the artist and his work. Perhaps it will be shown in Denver some day. If so, I will see an advertisement in the <u>rocky mountain news</u>.

       Our English teacher invited us to write about van Gogh in any way we wanted. One student wrote a poem called "awash in color." Another wrote a short story called "a day with Vincent." I wrote a review of the movie <u>Van Gogh</u>. The best responses will be published in the school literary magazine, <u>mountain school views</u>.

Apply

Answer each question by writing a complete sentence. Use correct capitalization and punctuation.

11. What would you name a film about the life of Vincent van Gogh? _____
    [The title must be underlined.]
    _____

12. What would you call a poem about the blue pitcher that van Gogh painted? _____
    [The poem will be marked by quotation marks.]
    _____

13. What would you title a book about the relationship between Vincent van Gogh and his brother Theo?
    [The title is underlined.]
    _____

    _____

14. What would you call a story about van Gogh's love of flowers? _____
    [The title gets quotation marks.]
    _____

15. What would you call a magazine that showed paintings of artists? _____
    [Underline]
    _____

16. The artist van Gogh sold only one painting during his life, although he is now famous. What would you name a song about this situation?
    [Quotation marks]
    _____

    _____

17. What would you call a film about the artist's passion for color? _____
    [Underline]
    _____

18. Name one newspaper that might carry a news story about a van Gogh exhibit.
    [Underline]
    _____

    _____

19. What title might a gardener give to a poem about van Gogh's pictures of flowers?
    [Quotation marks]
    _____

    _____

20. If a young artist were writing a song about van Gogh, what title might the song have?
    [Quotation marks]
    _____

    _____

Apostrophes

Learn

An **artist's** canvas is a flat surface, yet many artists create a feeling of depth within the picture. In these cases, viewers **don't** feel as if they are looking at flat surfaces.

Which boldfaced word shows possession or ownership? _____ artist's

Which boldfaced word is a combination of two words? _____ don't

> To form the **possessive** of a singular noun, add an **apostrophe** and **-s** (*girl's shoe*). For plural nouns that end in *s*, add an apostrophe (*birds' nests*) to form the possessive. For plural nouns that do not end in *s*, add an apostrophe and **-s** (*children's boots*). **Apostrophes** are also used in **contractions,** two words that have been shortened and combined.

Practice

Underline the correct word in parentheses. If the answer is a possessive, write **poss**. If the answer is a contraction, write the two words from which the contraction was made.

1. (Artist's/Artists') techniques vary for making pictures look three-dimensional.   poss

2. Although a painted road (does'nt/doesn't) vanish into the distance, it can appear to.   does not

3. In this picture, one (road's/roads') edges seem to meet in the distance.   poss

4. The (picture's/pictures') artist used this technique to suggest depth.   poss

5. Auguste Renoir (didn't/did'nt) use that method in this painting.   did not

6. Notice the size of the (women's/womens') heads that are closest to the viewer.   poss

7. They look larger than the (woman's/womans') head who sits behind them.   poss

8. They (are'nt/aren't) really larger, but closer objects look larger than ones farther away.   are not

9. Now look at the (mans'/man's) body on the right-hand side of the picture.   poss

10. It covers part of another person, so most (viewers'/viewer's) senses will react as if it were in front of the other person.   poss

11. An (artist's/artists') use of light can also suggest depth.   poss

12. All the (dancer's/dancers') light dresses seem to jump toward the viewer.   poss

Apply

Answers may vary. Possible responses appear below.

Rewrite these sentences. Replace boldfaced words with possessives or contractions.

13. **The lines that artists use** are an important element. _____

    Artists' lines are an important element.

14. An artist **does not** use a smooth curved line to suggest energy. _____

    An artist doesn't use a smooth curved line to suggest energy.

15. Short, choppy lines **do not** suggest peace and calm. _____

    Short, choppy lines don't suggest peace and calm.

16. **The lines of one artist** might be dark, heavy, and bold. _____

    One artist's lines might be dark, heavy, and bold.

17. **The lines of a different painter** might be loose and sketchy. _____

    A different painter's lines might be loose and sketchy.

18. **The lines of many Chinese artists** are created with pens and ink. _____

    Many Chinese artists' lines are created with pens and ink.

19. Often **they are** painted in traditional designs using black ink. _____

    Often they're painted in traditional designs using black ink.

20. The **shape of the brush** determines the type of line that it makes. _____

    The brush's shape determines the type of line that it makes.

21. The **techniques of painters** are different in the East and in the West. _____

    Painters' techniques are different in the East and in the West.

22. Chinese artists **will not** hold brushes in the same way they hold pencils; instead, the brushes
    are held upright.

    Chinese artists won't hold brushes in the same way they hold pencils; instead, the brushes

    are held upright.

23. **The ink Chinese artists use** comes in a block and must be ground into powder, then moistened with
    water in an inkstone.

    Chinese artists' ink comes in a block and must be ground into powder, then moistened with water

    in an inkstone.

24. An inkstone **is not** just any stone, and **it is** usually highly decorated. _____

    An inkstone isn't just any stone, and it's usually highly decorated.

Using Commas

Learn

a. Sister Wendy Beckett, an art historian, has written several books about art.
b. She has written about Italian, German, and French painters.
c. Her latest book is a colorful, informative volume.

Circle the comma or commas in each sentence.
In which sentence do commas separate three items in a series? _____ b.

What kind of words does the comma separate in sentence **c**? _____ adjectives

> A **series** is a sequence of three or more words, phrases, or clauses. A **comma** is used to **separate items in a series**. The last comma in a series goes before the conjunction (*and, or*). A comma is also used to separate **pairs of similar adjectives** (*colorful, informative volume*). To decide whether to put a comma between adjectives, read the sentence with the word *and* inserted between the adjectives. If the word *and* sounds natural, use a comma.

Practice

Add commas where they are needed in these sentences. Use the delete mark ( ) on commas that don't belong.

1. Pablo Picasso, Piet Mondrian, and Andy Warhol lived in the last century.

2. Their work is colorful, exciting, and individual.

3. The Blue Period, and the Rose Period of Picasso show different styles.

4. This creative, talented artist helped develop new art forms.

5. Piet Mondrian used such colors as red, yellow, and blue.

6. Much of his work focuses on shape, color, and balance.

7. Actresses, soup cans, and his own image were painted by Andy Warhol.

8. His distinctive, bold style is known as pop art.

9. Pop art celebrates both advertising, and entertainment.

10. It contains images from films, advertising, and even comic books.

11. Modern artists experiment with odd materials, strange colors, and unusual shapes.

12. I love viewing fresh, exciting art.

Rewrite each group of sentences as a single sentence. Use **and** or **or** to join the last two items in a series. Use commas where you need them. Answers will vary. Possible responses appear below.

13. Artists apply paint with brushes. They also use rollers. Some even use spray guns.

    Artists apply paint with brushes, rollers, and even spray guns.

14. An artist will select colors. Then the artist will mix the colors. Finally, the artist will apply the colors to the canvas or paper.

    An artist will select, then mix, and finally apply colors to the canvas or paper.

15. One artist might choose watercolors. One artist might use oil paints. Some artists prefer tempera.

    Different artists will choose watercolors, oil paints, or tempera.

16. Oil paints use pigment in some oil. The oil could be linseed oil or safflower oil. It could also be poppy oil.

    Oil paints use pigment in linseed oil, safflower oil, or poppy oil.

17. Artists choose their brushes based on the thickness of the paint. They also consider the size of the canvas and the style of the work.

    Artists choose their brushes based on the thickness of the paint, the size of the canvas,

    and the style of the work.

18. Modern artists may use oil paints. They may use watercolors. Many use acrylic paints. _____

    Modern artists may use oil paints, watercolors, or acrylic paints.

19. Acrylic paints can imitate oil paints. They can look like watercolors. They can imitate other types of paints as well.

    Acrylic paints can imitate oil paints, watercolors, and other types of paints.

20. Today, computers help modern artists draw images. Computers help them change images. Computers help them display images.

    Today, computers help modern artists draw, change, and display images.

More Uses for Commas

Learn

"Duane, tell me about this photo," said Mrs. Toro.

"Well, it's a portrait by Arthur Bedou, but that name may not help you," said Duane.

Who is being spoken to in the first sentence? _____Duane_____

What punctuation mark comes after the name? _____comma_____

What word introduces the second sentence? _____Well_____

What punctuation mark comes after it? _____comma_____

Underline the conjunction that joins the two parts of the second sentence.

What punctuation mark comes before it? _____comma_____

> **Commas** tell a reader where to pause. A comma is used to separate an **introductory word,** such as *yes* or *well,* from the rest of a sentence. It is also used with a conjunction to join **independent clauses** in a **compound sentence** and to separate a **noun of direct address** from the rest of a sentence. A noun of direct address names a person who is being spoken to.

Practice

Add the missing comma in each sentence. Then decide why the comma is needed. Write **I** for introductory word, **C** for compound sentence, and **D** for direct address.

1. "Actually, I have heard of Arthur Bedou," said Mrs. Toro.   I

2. "I grew up in New Orleans, and he worked there," she said.   C

3. "He was a photographer for half a century, but his name is not well known," she added.   C

4. "Mrs. Toro, I've seen his name in a book called *Early Black Photographers*," said Jenine.   D

5. "Jenine, does that book show any portraits by Cornelius Battey?" asked Duane.   D

6. "Yes, it has a portrait of two theater performers," said Jenine.   I

7. "Well, who were they?" Mrs. Toro asked. "Are they well known?"   I

8. "I didn't recognize their names, but you might," said Jenine.   C

9. "One was named Bob Cole, and the other was J. Rosamond Johnson," she said.   C

10. "Also, I think Battey photographed Booker T. Washington," said Mrs. Toro.   I

Apply

Rewrite the sentences, adding the words in parentheses. Be sure to use commas correctly.

11. Who was James VanDerZee? (Mrs. Toro) _____

Mrs. Toro, who was James VanDerZee?   OR   Who was James VanDerZee, Mrs. Toro?

12. He was a photographer in New York in the early 1900s. (well) _____

Well, he was a photographer in New York in the early 1900s.

13. He was a commercial photographer. (and he recorded life in Harlem) _____

He was a commercial photographer, and he recorded life in Harlem.

14. That photograph of the couple is really nice. (wow) _____

Wow, that photograph of the couple is really nice!

15. They are wearing those long fur coats. (and they have that fancy car) _____

They are wearing those long fur coats, and they have that fancy car.

16. VanDerZee was born in Lenox, Massachusetts. (but he mostly worked in Harlem)

VanDerZee was born in Lenox, Massachusetts, but he mostly worked in Harlem.

17. Did you notice how elegant his subjects look? (Duane) _____

Duane, did you notice how elegant his subjects look?

18. Does the man in the feathered hat look familiar? (Jenine) _____

Jenine, does the man in the feathered hat look familiar?

19. His name is Marcus Garvey. (and he was a political figure) _____

His name is Marcus Garvey, and he was a political figure.

20. VanDerZee's pictures are beautiful. (but people forgot him for a while) _____

VanDerZee's pictures are beautiful, but people forgot him for a while.

21. How nice that he lived long enough to see his popularity return. (gosh) _____

Gosh, how nice that he lived long enough to see his popularity return!

22. Few of these photographers are known to the general public. (unfortunately)

Unfortunately, few of these photographers are known to the general public.

Using Colons and Semicolons

Learn

  a. Some artists create paintings that hang in museums, others create works that appear in books.

  b. Some artists illustrate children's books; Steven Kellogg is one of these artists.

  c. An artist must study the following subjects: color, light, and design.

In which sentence are two independent clauses joined incorrectly with only a comma? _____ **a.**

In which sentence are two independent clauses joined by a semicolon? _____ **b.**

Which sentence uses a colon to introduce a list? _____ **c.**

> A **semicolon** (;) can be used instead of a comma and conjunction to separate the independent clauses in a **compound sentence**. A **colon** (:) can be used to introduce a list at the end of a sentence, to separate parts of references in a bibliography, and to separate hours and minutes in an expression of time.

Practice

Write a semicolon or a colon where it should be in each sentence.

  1. Steven Kellogg loves animals; they appear in many of his books.

  2. His mother and grandmothers read to him; this helped develop his love of books.

  3. Like other young people, he faced the following choices: career, education, and family.

  4. He loved art and drawing; he decided to become an artist.

  5. His ideas come from many sources: memories, experiences, and songs.

  6. He does not always stop work at 5:30; he sometimes works much later.

  7. Kellogg lives in an old farmhouse; he works on the top floor.

  8. He owns a Great Dane called Pinkerton; he has appeared in Kellogg's books.

  9. Kellogg uses many materials in his work: watercolors, acrylics, colored pencils, and brushes.

10. He sometimes includes his family in illustrations; he might draw his wife or his children.

11. As he works, Kellogg surrounds himself with art materials; he does not want to stop to search for something.

12. He has collected many toys and pictures; he keeps these in his workplace.

13. Steven Kellogg loves to draw many things: animals, trees, people, and architecture.

The colon has many uses in writing. Think about how the colon is used in these examples. Then draw a line from each example to the rule that it matches. Finally, write an example of your own to match each rule.

14. Book illustrators work with many people: art directors, agents, models, editors, and publishers.

15. Kellogg, Steven. *Pecos Bill*. New York: Morrow Junior Books, 1986.

16. Art class begins at 4:30.

17. LISA: It's a woodpecker!
STEVEN: Can you draw it?

18. Look carefully at book illustrations: you may see the artist's family.

19. Remember this advice from Kellogg: "Get as much practice as possible to develop your skills."

a. Use a colon to separate two independent clauses when the second explains the first.

b. Use a colon to introduce a list or series at the end of a sentence.

c. Use a colon after the speaker's name in a play.

d. Use a colon to separate the place of publication and the name of the publisher in a book reference in a bibliography.

e. Use a colon to separate hours and minutes in an expression of time.

f. Use a colon to introduce a quotation.

Answers will vary.

20. _____
_____

21. _____
_____

22. _____
_____

23. _____
_____

24. _____
_____

25. _____
_____

Using Hyphens and Parentheses

Learn

Vermilion is an orange-red mercuric sulfide (chemical formula HgS) used as a pigment in paint. The Chinese have used it for centuries. In fact, this vivid orange-red color is also called Chinese red or cinnabar.

Which word is explained in parentheses ( )? _____mercuric sulfide_____

Which compound word is linked with a hyphen? _____orange-red_____

Which word is separated into syllables with a hyphen at the end of a line? _____pigment_____

> **Hyphens** and **parentheses** are used to make writing clearer. Use a **hyphen** to:
> - separate the syllables in a word when you must break the word at the end of a line of text.
> - link the parts of some compound words, such as *great-grandmother*.
> - link some word pairs or groups of words that precede a noun and act as an adjective, such as *orange-red* color.
> - link the parts of numbers (written as words) between twenty-one and ninety-nine.
>
> Use **parentheses** to set off an explanation or an example.

Practice

Write **C** beside each sentence in which hyphens and parentheses are used correctly. Cross out hyphens and parentheses that are used incorrectly. If you are unsure whether a hyphen should be used to link parts of a compound word or adjective phrase, check a dictionary.

1. Organic pigments (those made from carbon compounds) can come from animals or vegetables. _____C_____

2. The so-called earth pigments include (ochres and umbers). _____

3. Mineral pigments come from naturally occurring minerals. _____

4. Artists also use many synthetic (manufactured) pigments. _____C_____

5. For example, fourth-century artists used white lead. _____C_____

6. Some pigments are highly toxic (poisonous) and must be used with care. _____

7. Zinc yellow is a bright greenish-yellow pigment. _____C_____

8. Some pigments are used in oil paints; others are used mainly in water-based paints. _____

9. Pigments vary greatly in their opacity (lack of transparency), color, and cost. _____C_____

Strategies for Writers—Conventions & Skills Practice **Unit 5**

Write a question to go with each answer below. Use a hyphen or parentheses in each question you write.   Answers will vary. Possible responses appear below.

10. A life-size painting might use three or four tubes of pigment. _____

How much paint might be used in a life-size painting?

11. You can see first-class paintings in a museum. _____

Where will you see first-class paintings?

12. These are all well-known Impressionist artists. _____

Are these well-known artists?

13. Early French painters seemed to love parasols (umbrellas used for shade). _____

Why so many parasols (those umbrellas the women are carrying) in the paintings?

14. Edouard Manet (a French artist) used blacks and whites well. _____

What is Edouard Manet (a French artist) known for?

15. A left-handed artist often starts painting on the right side of a canvas. _____

Does a left-handed artist work differently from a right-handed one?

16. Those bold strokes are the mark of a self-confident artist. _____

How might we recognize a self-confident artist?

17. Manet often applied paint with a palette knife (thin flexible spatula). _____

How was the palette knife (a thin flexible spatula) used?

18. Georges Seurat introduced pointillism (also called Neo-Impressionism), which involved making tiny dots on the canvas.

Who introduced pointillism (also called Neo-Impressionism)?

_____

19. In the 1880s, the most famous art school was probably L'Ecole des Beaux-Arts (School of Fine Arts) in Paris.

Why should we know about L'Ecole des Beaux-Arts (School of Fine Arts)?

_____

20. There are thirty-two paintings in this exhibit. _____

Did you say twenty-two or thirty-two paintings here?

Direct and Indirect Quotations

Learn

Lisa asked, "Who painted those animals?" Toby explained that early cave dwellers painted them.

Underline the sentence that shows a speaker's exact words. Circle the marks that begin and end this quotation. Circle the first letter of the quotation.

> A **direct quotation** is a speaker's exact words. Use **quotation marks** at the beginning and end of a direct quotation. Use a comma to separate the speaker's exact words from the rest of the sentence. Begin a direct quotation with a capital letter. Add end punctuation (period, question mark, exclamation point, or comma in place of a period) before the last quotation mark. An **indirect quotation** is a retelling of a speaker's words. Do not use quotation marks when the word *that* or *whether* comes before a speaker's words.

Practice

Write **I** after each indirect quotation and **D** after each direct quotation. Then add quotation marks, commas, and end marks to direct quotations. Draw three lines (≡) under lowercase letters that should be capitalized.

1. Toby said that the pictures were discovered in Spain in 1879.   I

2. He added, "the Altamira caves are filled with art."   D

3. Paulo said, "an entire herd of animals is painted onto the ceiling."   D

4. "But who painted them?" Lisa asked.   D

5. Paulo answered, "scientists believe that Stone Age people painted them."   D

6. "The scientists are still figuring out how they managed to do this," he added.   D

7. Then he reminded everyone that caves are pitch black inside.   I

8. "Remember that these were drawn thousands of years ago," he said.   D

9. Lisa wondered whether Altamira was the only cave with art.   I

10. Toby replied, "the Lascaux Caves in France also have beautiful paintings."   D

11. "The artists used powdered minerals in different shades," he explained.   D

12. "Hollow stone lamps lit up the inside of the cave," he continued.   D

13. He pointed out that these lamps used animal fat as fuel.   I

Apply

Rewrite each indirect quotation as a direct quotation. Rewrite each direct quotation as an indirect quotation. (There may be more than one right way to do this.) Be sure to use punctuation marks correctly.

14. Eli wondered whether all the colors were shades of brown. _____

Eli asked, "Are all these colors shades of brown?"

15. Gina explained that the colors included everything from white clay to black charcoal, as well as shades of brown, red, and yellow.

Gina explained, "They include everything from white clay to black charcoal, as well as shades of

brown, red, and yellow."

16. Paulo said, "Artists must have been uncomfortable in some of those narrow passageways."

Paulo observed that artists must have been uncomfortable in some of those narrow passageways.

17. Toby pointed out that scientists have found some sort of platform supports that the artists probably used.

Toby responded, "Scientists have found some sort of platform supports that the artists probably used."

18. Gina said, "Some artists painted with their hands, while others used drawing or engraving tools."

Gina said that some artists painted with their hands, while others used drawing or engraving tools.

19. Paulo wondered whether the pictures ever showed human beings. _____

Paulo asked, "Did the pictures ever show human beings?"

20. "Yes," said Toby, "but the drawings of the animals are better." _____

Toby said they did but that the drawings of animals are better.

21. Then he explained that the humans are shown as stick figures, while the animals are very detailed.

Then he explained, "The humans are just stick figures, while the animals are very detailed."

22. "I wonder why the drawings were made," said Eli. _____

Eli wondered why the drawings were made.

23. Lisa said that she loved the drawings because they were beautiful. _____

"I love the drawings because they are beautiful," commented Lisa.

Friendly Letters and Business Letters

1. 1225 Eye Street
Washington, D.C. 20025
March 9, 2003

Dear Anna, ___**2.**___

Our next stop is New York, and I'm really excited. We are going to see the Statue of Liberty and Fifth Avenue. We are also going to visit a lot of museums. I want to see the Museum of Natural History, and Ahmad wants to visit the Whitney Museum. I promise I'll send you a postcard from one of them! ___**3.**___

4. Love,
  Fatima ___**5.**___

There are five different parts of this letter. Two have already been numbered. Number the other three.

A **friendly letter** has five parts. The **heading** gives the writer's address and the date. The **greeting** includes the name of the person who will receive the letter. It begins with a capital letter and ends with a comma. The **body** gives the message. The **closing** is a friendly way to say good-bye. It ends with a comma. The **signature** is the writer's name. A friendly letter may include informal language.

A **business letter** is a formal letter written to an employer or a business. It has the same parts as a friendly letter, but it also includes the complete address of the person to whom the letter will be sent. Use a colon after the greeting in a business letter.

Practice

Use the boldfaced words in the rule box above to label the five parts of this friendly letter.

1. ___heading___ 90 Booth Avenue
Pasadena, CA 91107
March 30, 2003

Dear Fatima, **2.** ___greeting___

Have a great time in New York. We are going to drive down to San Diego to see the zoo there. Maybe I can see one of the koalas! I'll let you know.

3. ___body___

4. ___closing___ Your friend,

5. ___signature___ *Anna*

Rewrite this business letter correctly on the lines below. (Hint: The sender's address and the date go on the right. The business's or other receiver's address goes on the left. Check the rule box on page 105 if you need help.)

Whitney Museum of American Art 945 Madison Avenue New York, NY 10021. Dear Sir or Madam May 12, 2003 Please send me information about your hours, admission costs, and any special programs for families. We will be visiting your museum next month. Sincerely Jamal Nasser 770 Davis Avenue Pasadena, CA 91107

770 Davis Avenue

Pasadena, CA 91107

May 12, 2003

Whitney Museum of American Art

945 Madison Avenue

New York, NY 10021

Dear Sir or Madam:

Please send me information about your hours, admission costs,

and any special programs for families. We will be visiting your

museum next month.

Sincerely,

Jamal Nasser

Index of Skills

Index of Topics

Related to Content Areas

Social Studies

Science